THE VENGEANCE OF
THE DOLPHIN

The Vengeance of the Dolphin

Thomas Albert Roy

ILLUSTRATED BY
Rex Backhaus-Smith

THE BODLEY HEAD
LONDON SYDNEY
TORONTO

British Library Cataloguing
in Publication Data
Roy, Thomas Albert
The vengeance of the dolphin.
I. Title
II. Backhaus-Smith, Rex
823' .9'1J PZ7.R8144
ISBN 0-370-30215-X

©Thomas Albert Roy 1980
Illustrations © Rex Backhaus-Smith 1980
Printed in Great Britain for
The Bodley Head Ltd
9 Bow Street, London WC2E 7AL
by Redwood Burn Ltd, Trowbridge
Set in VIP plantin
First published 1980

For Jennifer: she carried out a
doubly vital task in the compilation
of this novel on the history of the
Aborigines of Cape York Peninsula.
She will be remembered.

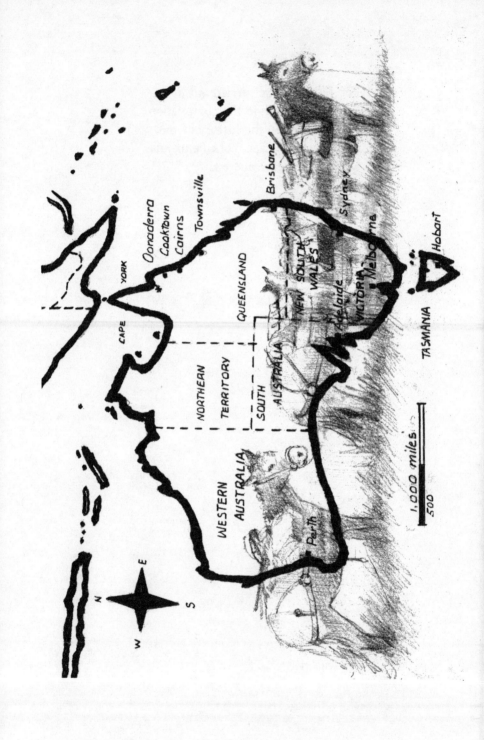

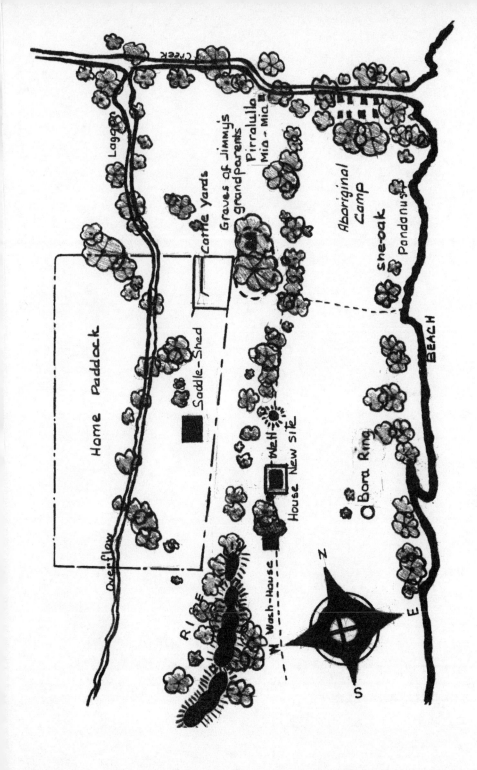

I

North of Cairns the vast loneliness of Australia's Cape York Peninsula stretches for hundreds of miles. To this day little has changed since the first white men saw it and some of its first inhabitants, the scattered tribes of Stone Age Aborigines.

In 1895 my paternal grandparents, Ebenezer and Agnes Brent, travelled overland along the east coast to reach and settle what is now this, my cattle property of Oonaderra. It was named after the Oona tribe of Aborigines who have their camp about a quarter of a mile farther north from this house, which my grandparents built and which I inherited from my father. I was a mere boy when that happened.

How vividly the memory of those boyhood days comes back to haunt me, reminding me how, by not owning up to the breaking of a tribal taboo, I made my own mother face death. Had I spoken the truth when asked, I could have prevented what happened to her; but I lied and thus brought on myself the agony of watching not only her suffering but the terrible ritual in the carrying out of the tribal vengeance.

To make matters worse it all began after a crippling drought, which not only almost wiped out our cattle and horses, but also caused a cholera outbreak among the Oona people. This killed off many of them and indirectly brought about the tragic death of my father when a drum of disinfectant fell on him in the saddle-shed over in the home paddock. At that time I was at boarding school in Brisbane. I had to leave school and come home to help Mum.

The drought eventually ended in storms and torrential

rain. Within a couple of weeks the native pastures recovered and life began to resume in all its fullness, giving us renewed hope for the future of Oonaderra.

After breakfast one morning, having nothing better to do or perhaps avoiding what other jobs needed doing around the place, I went into what my grandfather had used as an office-cum-gunroom. I still use it as such and Grand-dad's things are still in it—most important, an old-fashioned large tin trunk crammed with old diaries and all sorts of other odds and ends that had lain there over the years, forgotten . . . until I went to the trunk in the corner and lifted the lid to rummage among its crammed contents.

By piling the stuff from the trunk on the floor I got to the bottom of it without, as I thought, finding anything unusual until I caught sight of a fine crack running all round the bottom of the trunk. Curiosity made me run my index finger-nail along the crack . . . Suddenly, when I tried to withdraw my finger-nail the "bottom" of the trunk moved . . . A peculiar feeling came over me but I resisted it and lifted the false bottom. I looked beneath it . . . There, where it had lain for years and years, was a brass-bound log-book, about eight by six inches overall. It was locked with a small padlock holding tight the book's hinged clasps. There was no sign of a key. And beside the log-book was a strange, carved stick; it was about fifteen inches long and about two inches in diameter. It had a woven human-hair cord threaded through two holes, one at either end, to form a handle for carrying it. The carvings were totally meaningless to my eyes. It was the locked log-book that fascinated me.

I picked up the two objects and carried them over to the kitchen where my mother, her beautiful blond hair neatly combed back and wearing a hessian apron over her blue gingham frock, was kneading a batch of dough for our weekly bread-baking.

"Look, Mum!" I said excitedly, putting the two things on the table. "I found these in a secret compartment at the bottom of Grand-dad's old trunk."

She paused in her work, wiped her hands on her apron and picked up the log-book to examine it. She was quick to notice what I had failed to see: she lifted the brass padlock and looked at the brass band beneath it. Then she put the log-book on the table and holding up the padlock she said, "I have no idea whose initials they are, Jimmy."

I looked and saw etched into the brass band the initials J.F.

She went on, "Probably it was one of your grand-dad's old seafaring friends he knew before he left the sea to settle here on Oonaderra. As for that thing," she pointed at the carved stick, "it's no doubt some old Aboriginal curio your grandfather picked up somewhere; but why it should have been hidden away is beyond me. Maybe if you look through his old diaries you might come across a reference to why he hid these things away. There's probably some very simple explanation."

"But I'd like to find a key to open the log-book first, Mum," I suggested.

"There's no such key in this house, Jimmy; that I do know, because I would certainly have come across it during one of the regular clean-outs we've had over the years."

"All right, Mum," I answered. "But couldn't we just break the lock?"

"No, we will not," she said firmly. "That log-book has been in that old trunk for many a long year, so a wait of a little while longer won't make much difference. By and by we'll be going down to Cairns in the *Curlew* and then we can take the book with us and get a locksmith to cut a key for it."

The *Curlew* was, of course, our thirty-five foot, diesel-powered cabin cruiser which my father had bought some few months before his death. I was about to agree with her suggestion when she said, "Look, I want to get on with my baking, so take these things back where you found them and then you can go down to the boat and pump out the bilge that you said you and your friend Tajurra were going to do yesterday and didn't."

"OK, Mum," I answered and took the two things back to the gunroom. I put the log-book back into the secret compartment, then piled the old diaries and other things on top of the false bottom. The carved stick I left lying on my grandfather's table-top desk that stands by the window. The veranda outside faces north to the trees that fringe the banks of the fresh-water creek—Oonaderra's lifeline for our livestock—that runs out on to the beach and into the Coral Sea.

I was looking through the window when I caught sight of movement under the pandanus palms that front the beach facing the Oonas' permanent camp on the creek bank under the tall trees. It was Tajurra, my lifelong boyhood friend, who now walked from under the pandanus palms and stood on the beach. He was dressed like me—in the navy-blue shorts and short-sleeved shirt that my mother had made. Then the tall figure of Tajalli, his father, the leader of the Oona tribe, came striding out from the front of the camp to talk to his son. Even from a quarter of a mile away I could see that Tajalli was wearing his tribal lap-lap—a short skirt supported by a woven bark belt around his waist, from which dangled the usual close-packed woven bark cords that comprise the lap-lap proper. His mane of greying black hair was held in place by a woven human-hair headband befitting a tribal leader.

As I watched I saw Tajurra turn and come walking rapidly in the direction of the house. I closed the lid of the trunk and sat on it to wait for him. After a few minutes I heard him speaking to my mother in the kitchen who told him where I was.

"'Lo, Jimmy," he greeted me as he came into the room.

"What you do?" he asked, in our usual pidgin.

"Oh, just looking longa things longa this box," I answered. "Things belonga my grandfather in here. I find that funny fella stick." I pointed to where the carved stick lay on the desk-table.

He walked over to the desk, took one look at the stick and then backed away. With his eyes still fixed on it he stepped backwards and sat down beside me.

"What for you do that?" I asked. "That stick no more hurt you. What for you get fright?"

His eyes were still on the stick and his mouth was clenched shut.

"Come on, Tajurra!" I insisted. "Tell me what that silly fella stick means. Come on! Tell me!"

He turned his eyes away from the desk and answered, almost in a whisper, "Please, Jimmy, you no more ask me about that thing; him talk stick; me not know what 'im say. 'Im come from Burunji tribe. Tajalli know what that fella stick talk about. Me not know what it say, Jimmy."

"Then how you know stick come from Burunji tribe?" I persisted.

"You go look at that fella stick," he answered. "Burunji man make Burunji fish and make mark all the same on Burunji man's arm and on 'im chest."

I walked over to the desk and looked at the carvings on the stick: right in the middle of it, the unknown Burunji man who had made it had carved a fish and, just as Tajurra had said, above the carving were the tribal markings of the Burunji tribe: two horizontal incisions linked by an oblique line to form what looked like a Z. I later learned that this mark was used on each upper arm and chest of the men undergoing the initiation ceremony.

I turned to Tajurra and said, "What fella fish you call Burunji?"

He gestured with his hands to convey the motion of a creature swimming and frolicking on the surface of the sea and said, "Burunji big fella fish, chase sharks away."

Then, in a flash, I knew—the Burunji fish was the dolphin. The dolphin is the totemic god of the Burunji tribe, just as Oona, the great turtle, is the totemic god of the Oonas.

"All right, Tajurra," I said. "We no more talk about this fella talk stick. We go now longa boat, pump out water."

I slipped the stick into the top drawer of the desk and we headed over to the beach to get the dinghy to row out to the *Curlew*, munching the corned beef sandwiches that Mum had handed each of us with the warning, "Now don't go skylarking about in the boat you two! If you do, I won't let you go out there ever again on your own." She laughed and waved us on our way.

As we crossed from the house over to the bank that slopes down to the beach I was aware of Tajurra's silence.

We were about to descend the bank when Tajurra stopped me and said, "Jimmy, me feel big fella fright longa that Burunji talk stick; maybe bad fella debbil-debbil hide longa it."

"No!" I answered sceptically. "That fella talk stick no more got 'im debbil-debbil. You talk mad fella talk."

He was on the point of answering but didn't. Without another word we went down to the beach, pushed the *Curlew*'s dinghy into the water and rowed out to the boat.

For all the companionship that Tajurra offered I might as well have gone out by myself. We ran the engine to pump out the bilge and to charge the boat's batteries, and my friend still remained silent and uneasy, no matter how I tried to get his mind away from that cursed talk stick.

We rowed back and beached the dinghy, but instead of Tajurra returning with me to the house as he normally did, he made to set off along the beach back to the camp. I stopped him with an angry "Hey! What for you get mad longa me?"

He stopped, swung around and said, "More better me go see Tajalli, tell 'im you find Burunji talk stick. By and by me come see you longa house, tell you what Tajalli say, all right, Jimmy?"

"Oh, all right," I grudgingly agreed.

Again he turned to run back to the camp and again he stopped to face me with a beseeching look of fear on his usually happy-go-lucky face. "Jimmy," he said, "more better not let mother belonga you see 'im talk stick." Then in one swift movement he was gone, running like the wind to get to Tajalli, his father, with the news of the Burunji talk stick that was lying ... waiting ... in the home of the Brents.

I went back to the house to find Mum tidying up in the kitchen after her bread-making. But the smell of the bread and the rich aroma of treacle and raisins in a brownie she was also baking could not dispel the uneasy feelings I now had about that evil thing in the gunroom.

She greeted my return with an odd sort of smile as she said, "Have you and Tajurra been arguing or something, Jimmy?"

"No, Mum," I answered. "Why?"

"Oh, I'm not sure. Ever since you left the house I've had an odd sort of troubled feeling." Suddenly she put the palm of her hand over her eyes in a gesture of weariness. Then she sighed deeply and sat down, propping her elbows on the table and cupping her chin in her hands.

I went to her side. "Mum, what's the matter?" I asked.

"Oh, don't worry," she said, forcing a little smile. "I'll be right as rain in a minute or two."

And she was, or she pretended to be, five minutes later when I had made a pot of tea for us, and she took the aspirins I fetched from the medicine cabinet in her room.

I had never seen my mother look the way she did that morning. And to make matters worse, I could not, at first, shake off a feeling of dread that her having seen that talk stick had something to do with her sudden attack of weariness.

It was with a great feeling of relief that I saw her revive, presumably as a result of the aspirin, to become her usual healthy, normal self again.

At about three that afternoon Tajurra arrived at the back veranda where I was sitting in one of the wicker chairs at the veranda table. He was carrying by the gills a large sweetlip—a fine eating fish that abounds in the Great Barrier Reef waters.

"'Lo, Jimmy," he greeted me.

"'Lo, Tajurra," I answered. "Nice big fella fish, eh?"

He nodded and said, "Tajalli tell me take 'im this fella fish longa mother belonga you. Me take 'im longa her inside?"

"OK."

He went inside to Mum and returned a few minutes later carrying a plate of brownie slices and a jug of orange cordial with a couple of glasses. He was all smiles when he put the things on the table and sat himself in the chair opposite me.

Although he seemed happy enough while we ate the brownie and drank the cordial and kept our conversation focused on trivial small talk, I could sense an underlying mood of apprehension behind his obvious determination to keep our talk away from what was troubling him. He kept turning his head to look up at the trees at the top of the rise that slopes up from the back veranda. I knew that he was watching the lengthening shadows cast by the trees from the westering sun behind them. I also knew that his visit to the house was connected with more than the mere giving of a fish. Then suddenly he said, "Jimmy, me tell 'im Tajalli about you find 'im thing belonga Burunji tribe." He pointed north to indicate where that tribe has its permanent camp at the mouth of a fresh-water creek some fifty or so miles north of Oonaderra.

Obviously wanting to be over and done with anything to do with the dreaded talk stick he said, "Tajalli talk longa old men, talk longa me; 'im all get big fella fright, Jimmy. By and by Tajalli tell me, tell you hide that bad fella stick longa paper; no let mother belonga you see 'im; tell you bring 'im stick longa camp longa morning."

"What for he want 'im stick longa camp?" I asked.

He refused point blank to be drawn into any discussion that could involve him in revealing a tribal secret. I knew as well as he did that death was the punishment for revealing such secrets to anyone outside the tribe, if the tribal elders ever found out about it.

Impatiently, I said, pointing to the three vertical cicatrices on both his upper arms and the three in the centre of his chest, "You got 'im that fella mark; that fella mark say you man belonga your people."

He nodded. Then I pointed to the cicatrice on my own upper right arm which he had made the year before on the morning after the tribal elders had carried out his initiation into manhood. On that morning we had mingled our blood and drunk it, which had made me also an initiated man as well as a blood brother of Tajurra in the eyes of Tajalli and the elders.

I said, "You man, me man; suppose you tell me what Tajalli and old men talk about longa that Burunji stick, me not tell anybody about it. Come on! Talk!"

After arguing with him for some time I said angrily, "All right, you no want tell me what Tajalli and old men talk about; me no more talk longa you; no more take 'im talk stick longa camp longa morning!" I made to get up but he stopped me.

"Jimmy, please, me feel big fella fright. You no more tell anybody what me tell you?"

I agreed and, dropping his voice to a strained whisper, he

told me the story of how, a long time ago, a Burunji man had killed a woman on Oonaderra and how Tajalli and other Oona tribesmen had found her body. They had given her a Burunji burial high up in the hollow of a stringybark tree at a place called Cannon Ball Rock, out along the track that follows the creek bank through the open forest country all the way to the far parts of Oonaderra's boundaries. He then said he had been told that the killing of the woman was only part of the story that lay hidden in the symbolic carvings of the Burunji talk stick.

I asked him if the Burunji man who had murdered the woman had been put to death in accordance with tribal law and he answered, "No, Jimmy; that fella Burunji man run away longa ranges; 'im hide longa there all the time now, no more let other man catch 'im."

So I learned that the man had become an outcast from his tribe and that he would be put to death if ever he set foot on either Oona tribal territory or on his own Burunji territory. As a consequence, Cannon Ball Rock and that stringybark tree containing the bones of the murdered woman had become taboo to all Aborigines.

No amount of persuasion, however, could get me the name of that man from the now trembling Tajurra. He got up and, first looking apprehensively at the long shadows of the trees and then beseechingly at me, he whispered, "Please, Jimmy, you my brother; you help me; you bring 'im Burunji talk stick longa camp longa morning. Please, Jimmy?"

"OK," I agreed.

Those long shadows denoting the approach of sundown were all that Tajurra needed to urge him to get going for the safety of the camp and the fires of the Aboriginal families around their mia-mia shelters . . . the fires that kept away the debbil-debbils lurking in the darkness beyond.

We bid each other "So long" and he left, running like the wind, secure in the knowledge that his lifelong friend would stand by him no matter what happened the next morning.

2

Over our dinner of delicious baked sweetlip and potato-chips that evening my mother said, "I hope you and Tajurra haven't made any plans for tomorrow, Jimmy."

"Why?" I asked, suspecting that she was preparing me for some job around the property she wanted doing. And I guessed right. She answered, "I want you to go out in the morning to see how the cattle and horses are doing and check on them for ticks. We can't let them go too long if the ticks are bad or it will take twice as long to get them into good condition again; so, if you like, you can take Tajurra along with you. I'll make up a packet of sandwiches and you can take a billy-can to make tea."

"Gee, thanks, Mum," I agreed with a sigh of relief at not having to chop wood or do some other chore that would keep me under her eye around the house. "Will it be all right," I asked, "if I let Tajurra ride one of the horses and I ride Creamy?"

"Yes; the horses in the home paddock, when I saw them a couple of days ago, seemed to be in fair enough condition to be ridden again; but mind you take Creamy gently and no galloping; you can saddle up Dad's black gelding for Tajurra and tell him to take things gently, too."

"I will, Mum!" I assured her. "We won't go knocking the horses about, Mum. I promise."

"All right, then," she said. "And if you take your rifle along, see that you don't shoot anything and leave it wounded in the bush for the crows to get at it." (That was her way of enforcing my dead father's dictum that if anything were shot on the property it must never be left to die in pain.)

In my talk with my mother over dinner I was careful not to mention that I was taking the message stick over to the Oonas' camp to let Tajalli see it. If I had told her, she would have questioned me about it, and, being Mum, she would have put a stop to anything she thought might be the cause of further trouble on Oonaderra; she had already suffered enough from the drought and the death of my father as well as all the other misfortunes that had visited the property over the past twelve months. Now, in the light of what took place later, I can see the stupidity of my behaviour.

The following morning I went over the rise to the home paddock to catch and saddle up the black gelding and Creamy, my Arab pony, who were kept in the paddock along with old Nellie, the pack-horse. I had with me my .32 repeater rifle and a skinning knife, in case I could bag a wallaby and take the tail home for Mum to cook it. The message stick I had wrapped in a sheet of old newspaper. I was halfway up the rise at the back of the house when Mum called out, "Hey, Jimmy, don't forget to pick up your sandwiches and the billy-can for your lunch before you leave."

"OK, Mum," I called back to her. "I'll go over to the camp and pick up Tajurra first." I went over the rise and down the other side into the home paddock.

All I had to do to catch the horses was to get two bridles out of the saddle-shed and walk back outside to the hitching rail and call out, "Kip, kip, kip; come on, kip, kip, kip."

Creamy came galloping up to the rail with the black gelding following and old Nellie ambling along in the rear. They lined up while I fished in my pocket for the three aniseed lollies I had brought to reward them.

First I gave Creamy a lolly; he nickered with pleasure and

let me slip the bit into his mouth and the bridle over his head. I dropped the reins over the rail and repeated the performance with the gelding; then I gave the last lolly to old Nellie.

I was just going back into the shed to get the saddles when Tajurra came racing over from the camp apparently alarmed that I was leaving without letting him know where I was going.

"'Lo, Jimmy," he greeted me.

"'Lo, Tajurra. What for you come here?" I answered.

He got his breath back, to tell me that Tajalli and the old men were waiting for me. Tajalli had seen me going over the rise and thought I had forgotten my promise to bring the message stick to the camp that morning.

I assured Tajurra I had not forgotten and took him inside the shed where I had put the stick, the rifle and the knife on the work-table. Then he helped me saddle up the horses, evidently very relieved and happy to be invited to go with me on a ride of inspection. But no amount of persuasion on my part could get him to touch or even look at what was wrapped in the newspaper.

To save time I said to Tajurra, "You go longa house, missus give you tucker and billy-can. Me go longa camp, see Tajalli."

"All right, Jimmy," he answered. "Me get 'im tucker, see you quick."

He mounted and rode over the rise to the house, while I hopped up on to Creamy and rode over to the camp to see Tajalli with the rifle slung over my shoulder and the wrapped message stick clutched in my free hand.

I rode into the centre of the camp, which was deserted because the hunting and fishing parties had already left and all the women and children were out on their allotted tasks of daily food gathering. I rode on through the rows of thatched

22

beehive-shaped mia-mia shelters and found Tajalli with Trokka, the oldest of the tribal elders, sitting with the rest cross-legged in a circle on the sand in front of Tajalli's mia-mia.

"'Lo, Jimmy," they greeted me.

"G'day," I answered and handed down the wrapped stick into Tajalli's upstretched hand.

Not another word was spoken while Tajalli unwrapped the carved stick. There was a peculiar atmosphere that communicated itself to me in an uncomfortable feeling of anxiety in the pit of my stomach.

Something made me look up into the fronds of the pandanus palms above ... dangling there on a plaited human-hair cord was a bone. I had seen that cord and that bone somewhere else ... suddenly I remembered ... it was the self-same cord and bone that Tajalli had used to exorcize the debbil-debbils from the Oonas' sacred Bora Ring after the elders of the tribe had exhorted their god Oona, the great turtle in the sky, to lift the agony of drought and death on Oonaderra. In that bone (the thigh bone, I think, of an Australian native cat) resides, so the Aborigines believe, a potent power of witchcraft strong enough to kill a man when it is used in conjunction with the dreaded Kadiatcha shoes that leave no clue on the ground that an evil spirit has encircled a doomed man's mia-mia and that he has been "sung" to death in the dreaded ceremony of the Pointing of the Bone.

Even the pony was uneasy. He kept backing away from the group and it was as much as I could do to keep him from wheeling and bolting away from the sensation of dread that hung over us in the shade of the palms. At the same time I could not keep my eyes off the thing dangling there.

A sudden "Wah!" broke the silence and helped to drag my gaze down to the group now bent over the message stick

23

where Tajalli had placed it in the sand. The old men were staring spellbound at what was carved on the Burunji tribe's message stick.

Tajalli then passed the stick to Trokka who held it in his hands while he slowly turned it to scan the message revealed by the intricate symbols carved on it—a message that could be read only by those eyes it was intended for. I knew this because the generally accepted method of communication between the tribes is "smoke talk"—sending messages by smoke signals that are entrusted to one male member of the tribe who is responsible for the accuracy of interpreting what the tribal elders instruct him to say.

One by one the elders took and scanned the stick. Then it was wrapped again in the newspaper and given to Tajalli who spoke rapidly to the gathering in Oona. They nodded in agreement and all eyes turned to look at me, still uneasy and wondering what was going on in their minds. Holding the wrapped stick behind him, Tajalli got up and said, "Jimmy, this fella stick talk all about bad things, long time ago; 'im talk all about grandfather belonga you; talk about another white man come longa Oonaderra; this man bad fella white man, make plenty trouble longa Burunji people; 'im steal Burunji woman belonga Kammaluk; 'im try steal thing longa bag belonga Kammaluk. Altogether this fella white man, bad man, Jimmy."

"Who this fella Kammaluk?" I asked and he answered, "'Im all the same me, Jimmy—boss fella belonga Burunji people."

So I learned that Kammaluk was, like Tajalli to the Oona people, an elected leader of the Burunji people. But Tajalli would not tell me more about the white man's attempt to steal something from Kammaluk's bag. I took this to mean a bag similar to the one in which Tajalli keeps the sacred tribal objects of stones and assorted mummified creatures. These

24

are the very precious things with which Aboriginal witchcraft is invoked in many of their secret ceremonies, which only the eyes of initiated men of the tribe may see and which must never be shown to others, especially women, and never, under any circumstance, to white people.

I then said to Tajalli, "That fella white man maybe dead now; Kammaluk maybe dead."

"No," Tajalli answered firmly. "White man no more die yet; Kammaluk old man, 'im no more die yet. By and by me talk smoke talk longa Burunji people tell 'im talk stick stop longa Oonaderra long time. Oona men keep 'im stick, by and by send 'im back longa Burunji people."

"No, Tajalli," I remonstrated. "Suppose mother belonga me find out me give talk stick longa you, she get mad, make plenty trouble longa me."

He just answered quietly, "Mother belonga you see this fella talk stick?"

"No," I lied promptly.

"She not know you bring 'im longa me, Jimmy?"

"No," I again answered, this time truthfully.

"All right," he said, "maybe by and by you get this fella stick back; you no more talk about it longa mother belonga you, eh?"

"Oh, all right," I agreed, glad to get the business over and done with; anyway, what difference could it make, I thought, if I never saw the trouble-making thing again; my mother would never miss it. She had regarded it as nothing important.

Out of the corner of my eye I saw Tajurra on the gelding trotting over from the house, so I said to Tajalli, "All right Tajurra come longa me see cattle and horses no got ticks, Tajalli?"

"All right, Jimmy," he answered. "See you by and by."

"OK, then." I wheeled the pony round and waved to

Tajurra to come on as I set off at a trot along the track that follows the creek bank all the way out to the far parts of the run.

After a while I slowed down to a walk to let Tajurra catch up with me. When he did he was all smiles, happy not only with the lunch things Mum had given him but also the slab of brownie she had given him to share with me on the ride. He broke it in two, gave half to me and said, "Mother belonga you tell me tell you come home before sun go down; she say suppose you not come home quick, she send you back longa school quick smart."

"Oh yair!" I grinned. "Suppose we no get back longa sundown, I tell her you make me late talking mad fella talk."

And so we rode steadily at a fast walk to save the horses and to enjoy the scenery of the green belly-high grass we were travelling through to reach some of the cattle and horses we could see away in the distance among the trees of the open forest country.

We had been going about ten minutes or so when Tajurra looked back and exclaimed, "Hey, Jimmy, Trudy come longa us!"

I looked back to see Trudy, our blue cattle dog, racing along the track behind us; my mother had let her off the chain at the house knowing the dog would set out after the black gelding, as she had always done whenever my father had rode the horse around the property.

"Oh, well," I told Tajurra. "Maybe 'im dog bail up big fella wallaby, maybe get 'im kangaroo."

So we rode on with her trotting along behind us.

The recent good rain that had fallen on Oonadera had certainly brought a resurgence of life to the property; everywhere we heard the calls of currawongs, magpies, sulphur-crested cockatoos, parrots and every other kind of bird that wheeled in the air above us; we could see others in

26

the grass on either side of the track, gorging on the bountiful harvest of seeding plants and fruiting native trees.

Half a mile farther on we reached Cannon Ball Rock, a massive granite boulder that had no doubt rolled down from the distant ranges in some prehistoric cataclysm millions of years ago. I now knew why that huge spherical rock and the tall stringybark tree that towered above it had been declared taboo to all Aborigines because of what had been put in the stringybark tree long before Tajurra and I were born. The fact that Tajurra had always known there was a debbil-debbil in that place explained why he had never allowed himself ever to get too close to it in the past.

Now, when we reached the Rock, Tajurra suddenly wheeled his horse off the track into the grass. He believed, and still believes, the place to be haunted by a debbil-debbil—the spirit of the Burunji woman who was murdered there and whose body was hidden in a hole in the tree which I could see some twenty or so feet up the massive trunk.

I stopped and called out to Tajurra who rode on until he was well away from the place of the evil spirit. He looked back at me over his shoulder. I was about to tell him to stop being a fool and come back when he called out, "Please, Jimmy, that bad fella place; come away quick! Please, Jimmy!"

No matter how I tried to persuade him, Tajurra would tell me no more than that the bones of the Burunji woman were there in the tree; not another word could I get out of him.

We kept moving steadily onwards until we reached the first of the cattle and horses strung out by the side of the track. We rode slowly at a walking pace so as not to startle the stock which, however, ignored our passing because they did not associate the slowly moving horses with the riders on their backs.

It was a welcome sight to see that the grazing animals were tick-free, and by about midday we had gone far enough and seen enough to convince me it was time to boil the billy to make tea for our lunch. There was no need to go farther to find out that the stock was indeed safe to leave for the time being. So we made our way down to the edge of the creek for water and settled down in the shade of the trees to boil the billy.

We were talking and enjoying our sandwiches and tea when Tajurra looked up and pointed to the sky above the trees and said, "Look, Jimmy, Brolga."

I looked up and saw circling against the backdrop of the blue sky two "Native Companions"—members of the family of Australian cranes. Tajurra had used the Aboriginal word "Brolga". The term "Native Companion" is an Australian colloquialism, describing the habits of the birds in their courtship when they frolick and "dance" on the ground. We watched the two big bluey-grey birds as they zoomed down to the sand a little way up the creek.

We were watching them intently as they began their up-and-down hopping and flapping of wings when suddenly Tajurra looked back in the direction we had come and whispered, "Oona man say, 'Hurry, quick! Come back!'"

That urgent summons could only be attributed to the Aborigines' ability to communicate with each other through the means of extra sensory perception. I didn't question him. We just put out the fire and headed for home. I knew full well that when we reached the Oonas' camp Tajurra would be proved right.

During the whole of our ride up creek, Tajurra and I had not sighted a single kangaroo or wallaby, although it was more than likely that there were wallabies feeding unseen in the high grass. It was disappointing for us when we had hoped to bag a wallaby, particularly for Tajurra who would have been able to justify his standing in the eyes of the tribe by bringing home fresh meat to add to the communal supply provided by the hunting and fishing parties. We knew, of course, that Trudy, the dog, would have soon bailed up any wallaby if she had caught its scent or spotted it in the grass by the side of the track, but she just kept behind us trotting along quietly.

Suddenly the dog raced past us and kept going in the direction of the distant Oonas' camp. We pulled up and listened. Faintly in the distance we could hear the sound of the barking camp dogs. I looked at Tajurra who said, "Dogs bail up big fella pig, Jimmy; me think 'im catch that big fella pig longa Big Scrub."

The Big Scrub is a two-hundred-acre area of rain forest some distance behind the Oonas' camp and extending northwards from the other side of the creek to form a "pocket" of dense forest jungle totally different from the open grassy forest country.

In that dense pocket of scrub there are strange creatures: cassowaries, wild pigs and the deadly Taipan snake. There are also weird plants and vines, including the vicious gympie-gympie stinging tree.

We continued on our way at a steady walk to spare the horses, but we were impatient to see if the hunting party had indeed got a "big fella pig".

By the time we reached the trees fringing the Oonas' camp, the hunting party were there and had carried the kill into the centre of the camp where all the tribe had gathered round it. We dismounted and hitched the horses to a couple of saplings. Tajurra got the skinning knife from the saddle-bag and we made our way into the centre of the camp through the noisy, happy people milling around a wide sheet of bark on which lay the carcase of the pig—a huge black-and-white boar—with Tajalli standing beside it. Tajalli spotted us and he called out to Tajurra to bring the skinning knife to him.

Without wasting time, Tajalli took the knife and began the

cutting up of the pork. First he cut one back leg away from the carcase. Then he cut deep around the heavy, upper portion as skilfully as any butcher, and finally drew away from the bone a fat piece of the meat. Then he straightened up from his task and said to me, "This nice fella piece, Jimmy, me give mother belonga you, eh?"

"Gee, thanks, Tajalli," I answered.

He smiled, turned to a young girl in a woven bark lap-lap and spoke to her in the usual familiar pidgin, "Monabi, get coolamon, take meat longa Missus."

The girl disappeared. When she came back with the coolamon Tajalli put the slab of pork into it and sent her running over to the house to deliver it to my mother.

Tajalli then nodded to Tajurra who went over to him. With the laughter and excited talking going on all around, it was impossible for me to know what was being said to Tajurra who came back to me and nudged me to follow him. We made our way to where the horses were tethered at the camp's edge.

We stood for a while talking about the happenings of the day and then he said, "Jimmy, Tajalli tell me old men not give talk stick back longa you."

"Why?" I asked, not a little angry. It was unusual conduct for the tribal elders to do anything which might be troublesome to white people. He just said quietly, "Tajalli say old men know what that bad fella talk stick say; suppose Burunji people know where that fella stick be now, altogether too much trouble come longa Oonaderra. More better let old men talk longa Burunji people by and by, Jimmy. Old men stop trouble come longa this place."

"Oh, all right," I answered peevishly, thinking that the elders were treating me as though I were a child; but I knew deep down that they were right in not wanting any more trouble than we had had already. So after a few moments I added, "Maybe Tajalli and old men talk true, Tajurra; maybe that mad fella talk stick bring more bad fella debbil-debbils longa this place, eh? Maybe Tajalli and old men stop 'im do that, eh?"

"Yes, Jimmy; Tajalli say big fella bad debbil-debbil stop inside that talk stick; suppose 'im Burunji old men know that stick stop longa Oona people, by and by Burunji old men make big fella corroboree, tell 'im Burunji god come longa Oona people, kill 'im all. That fella talk stick bad debbil-debbil too much, Jimmy." The reason for Tajurra's call home became clear.

"Well, all right, Tajurra," I said. "Me better go now, put horses longa home paddock." I was about to mount the pony when Monabi came hurrying back from the house carrying in her coolamon a big tin of liquorice all-sorts my mother had given her to share among the Oonas. Tajurra, the moment he saw the tin as she was passing us, eagerly asked her for "a lolly" but she ran on laughing and holding the tin out of his reach.

Then he turned back to me to say, "Tajalli make smoke talk longa morning, Jimmy; talk longa Burunji old men. You no more tell Tajalli me tell you, eh?"

"OK," I agreed. "See you longa morning." I hopped up on the pony, gathered up the reins of the gelding and trotted off for the home paddock with Trudy following me.

I let the horses go and took Trudy home.

Perhaps it was my appetite and gorging on the pork which caused the terrible nightmares that haunted me in my sleep that night; perhaps my mind had been conditioned by what Tajurra had told me about the forces of evil that might be released by the message stick now in the hands of the Oonas.

Or perhaps my fears that night were the direct result of those forces of evil already gathering momentum in the minds of the Oona tribe's elders for solution on the morrow.

Whatever the cause of the nightmares, it was just as well that I could not foresee then the things that were to come, the rituals that I was to witness deep in the wilderness of Cape York Peninsula, and the terrible retribution that would follow.

3

Over our dinner of roast pork that evening I had told Mum the stock were getting into good condition and there would be no need, for at least another month, to worry about having to dip the cattle against tick infestation. That relieved her mind, because she did not want to have all the confusion of mustering the cattle and all the other chores of cooking for the Oona men who would have to do the work. She was not feeling up to that responsibility just then. The trouble was really her state of health; ever since the day she had become ill after seeing that cursed Burunji message stick, she had had recurring bouts of listlessness.

But the following morning my nightmares and fears for her soon faded in the brilliant hues cast by the sun I could see emerging on the horizon as I dressed and looked out of my open window across the Coral Sea. To my surprise I saw Tajurra hurrying across to the house. I met him at the back steps and he handed me my skinning knife with an apologetic "Tajalli sorry he forget give knife back belonga you."

I took it and laughed. "No more get sorry," I assured him. "I forget that knife too!"

Now that the good name of his father had been restored, Tajurra grinned and said, "Monabi tell Tajalli mother belonga you want woman help longa washing clothes. Tajalli send two women by and by help longa washing."

I suddenly remembered that it was wash day and that I was responsible for getting the wash-copper fire lit and the copper filled for boiling the clothes so, taking advantage of Tajurra, I suggested, "You like have breakfast longa me?"

"Too right!"

"All right, then; you help me fix boiler up, eh?"

"Too right, Jimmy!" he repeated. "We do that now?"

"No; come in. Me tell missus you help her, you get tucker like me."

He followed me into the kitchen where my mother was already preparing an omelet of canned tomatoes and egg pulp.

"'Lo, Missus," Tajurra said a little shyly.

"Oh, hello, Tajurra!" she exclaimed in surprise and immediately saved me the trouble of telling her why I had invited him in without warning. She said, "You like tucker longa us, Tajurra?"

"Too right ... er ... " He paused as he realized he was doing what Noola, his mother, and Tajalli, his father, had repeatedly warned him never to do—impose on the goodwill of my mother or take any unfair advantage of the fact that my mother and I were the only white people on the property.

Tajurra quickly recovered himself and said, "Thanks, Missus. You give breakfast, me help Jimmy fix fire longa boiler."

"Well, now," she answered, stirring the big omelet in the frying pan on the stove. "That's good. Now sit down the pair of you and get started."

Neither of us needed any urging to get stuck into that breakfast. But I must say that we did wait until she had taken her place at the head of the kitchen table before starting on that delicious omelet with toast and canned butter and tea to wash it down.

It's a peculiar thing with Aborigines—they never guzzle food. They eat quietly in the knowledge that time matters little when the pleasure of eating food can be prolonged—a pleasure that is all the greater when compared with the endless struggles they have endured over the centuries even to survive at all.

We talked and ate and discussed all sorts of things, including the catching of the wild pig the day before. Then after a good half hour at the table we rose, Tajurra again thanked "Missus" for the breakfast, and we went out to the wash-house to get things started, leaving Mum to cook more omelet in readiness for the arrival of the two women from the camp to help with the washing.

While Tajurra and I got the copper going and stacked more wood alongside it for the women to keep the fire going, we talked about the "smoke talk" that Tajalli was going to make that morning at a time when he expected the wind from the sea to die down sufficiently to allow him to transmit the message he was to send to the Burunji elders.

I was busy filling the boiler with buckets of water from the rainwater tank at the side of the wash-house when Tajurra remarked, "By and by Tajalli put tumoolu longa creek, catch fish, Jimmy."

"Tumoolu?" I asked in surprise, because I recognized the word as one used by the Oonas to denote an annual event.

I knew that the word also meant a native vine that grows in the rain forest and is often used by the tribal Aborigines to catch fish in the fresh-water creeks or waterholes when the water is slow-moving enough to retain the soporific drug that the plant exudes from its sap and leaves. This drug, or chemical, stuns the fish which then rise to the surface and are easily caught. The fish can then be eaten without any ill effects.

Tajurra told me that a search party was going out into the scrub to collect the vine and that we could go along and watch the men when they selected a spot in the creek to use the vine. But we were not to go near the beach while Tajalli was engaged in sending whatever message the Oona elders gave him in his "smoke talk" with the Burunji elders in their camp many miles away to the north of Oonaderra at the mouth of a creek that, like Oonaderra's, runs into the Coral Sea.

It didn't worry me that Tajalli had forbidden us to be on the beach because I had already decided to row out to the *Curlew* and I knew that my father's high-powered binoculars were on board. I would be able to see clearly what Tajalli did in sending his smoke signals from the beach; as Tajurra informed me, his father would be right out in front of the pandanus palms. That was why there were no Oona fishing parties along the beach that day. The "smoke talk" could be witnessed only by the elders of the Oona tribe at their end and the Burunji elders at the other. I had yet to see how Tajalli could warn the other tribe of what was to take place.

By the time we had got the fire going well and the copper full we saw the Oonas, men, women and all the young ones, leaving the camp and heading up creek. The two women who were to help with the wash were on their way over to the house.

I said to Tajurra, "You want to come longa me, longa boat?"

"No, Jimmy!" he answered in alarm. "Suppose Tajalli see me go longa boat, he get mad, say me look longa smoke talk; more better me go now longa men longa scrub, help 'im get tumoolu, catch fish by and by. You come longa creek see men catch fish by and by?"

"Yes," I answered readily and the next moment he was running up over the rise with a "By and by, Jimmy, see you longa creek." He disappeared down over the other side of the rise.

I glanced over at the *Curlew* and saw that the sea would soon begin to run out on the ebb tide; later the breeze would begin to lessen, so I called out, "Mum, will it be all right now for me to row out and check the boat to see if everything is OK?"

"Yes, if you must," she called out from the kitchen. "But mind you don't go doing anything stupid out there. And see that you get back here in time for lunch."

"OK, Mum. I will. Thanks."

I raced across and down to the dinghy moored out from the beach. In a matter of minutes I was aboard the *Curlew* and, after a quick inspection to find everything in proper order, I got the binoculars out of the cabin locker and then perched myself up in the steering seat with a clear view through the cabin window in all directions. I wondered about the two women with Mum, but then I realized that Tajalli would know that their view of the beach in front of the camp would be blocked by the house while they worked in the wash-house.

I trained the glasses on the beach at the front of the palms and saw that a pile of logs had been built in readiness on the sand that forms the creek bank.

By the side of the prepared fire was a big mound of green mangrove twigs and leaves. But there was no sign of Tajalli or anyone else. I could only idly wait, and so began to swing the glasses in a circle, watching the sea birds flying over a flotilla of pelicans feeding around the water along the distant reef.

Suddenly, when I again focused the glasses on the beach near the prepared fire, I saw Tajalli and Trokka emerge from the screen of the high roots of the palms. They were wearing lap-laps and Trokka was carrying a glowing fire stick. Tajalli was carrying a flat sheet of bark about two feet square.

The old man thrust the fire stick into the base of the logs and almost immediately the kindling there caught alight and the fire blazed up for a couple of minutes, then settled into a glowing mass of coals and low flames. Every detail of what they were doing was as plain to me as if I were standing beside them.

Then I became aware of a distinct change in the sound of

the water lapping against the sides of the boat. The breeze had dropped almost to nothing and the boat was riding at her moorings in silence.

I again became intent on watching the two men. I saw them exchange nods, and then Trokka picked up a bundle of the green mangrove twigs and leaves and dropped them on the fire.

At once a column of dense white smoke rose straight upwards. With a quick movement Tajalli held the sheet of bark over the rising smoke and broke it once, twice, several times into measured "puffs", some long, some short.

When the message was apparently complete, he stopped and the two men stood watching the skyline to the north. From time to time as they waited they kept looking out to sea, which, of course, prompted me to do likewise. To my surprise, when I trained the glasses over the sea I saw what at first I took to be human heads bobbing about.

Alternately watching the two men and the things bobbing in the sea I was on the point of giving up watching the men when suddenly, as I swung the glasses back to them, I saw Trokka pointing excitedly to the north. I swung the glasses north to see what it was—nothing! Yet they, with their acute vision, had spotted something. They stood absolutely still reading the sky to the north for the answer they had been waiting for.

Obviously the Burunjis were answering with their own "smoke talk" which I could not see, even with the glasses. No doubt the delay had been caused by the Burunji elders having to build a fire before they could send a message in reply.

I then became engrossed in watching Trokka and Tajalli repeating further "smoke talk" in answer to what they were receiving from the Burunjis. In my watching I lost track of time until I saw that the two men seemed to have finished their "smoke talk", because they had left the fire to die down and were walking to the sea's edge to watch those strange objects floating in the water beyond the channel that leads through the reef.

I didn't want Tajalli to know that I was on the boat, so I stayed on board until the two men left the beach and went back into the camp. Then I rowed ashore and returned to the wash-house to tell Mum about the things floating in the sea.

She was too busy with the two women getting the washing done to pay much heed or to worry about anything else for the time being. So she sent me into the house to get the stove going for lunch for the four of us.

After lunch I slipped away to the beach to see if the floating objects had come in any closer to shore—they had! Scores of them were being carried up the channel on the incoming tide—coconuts!

And I was not the only one down there at the water's edge; a dozen or more of the women and kids were waiting to grab the manna from the sea just as soon as it came close enough. The laughter and merriment was enough to scare off all the gulls and pelicans that had been busily fishing among the nuts until the women arrived.

The harvest of nuts from the sea was the result, I think, of the recent storms that had brought the rains to Oonaderra and had also obviously dislodged the coconuts off the wild coconut palms on the islands that dot the reef and coastline.

There were enough nuts in the sea to keep the Oonas in good food for a long time to come. But I didn't wait to watch the women and kids gathering the nut harvest, I went on up creek, and there found a group of the Aboriginal men strung out over the Crossing with three-pronged fishing spears in their hands.

I answered their "'Lo, Jimmy" greeting and was about to go over into the Big Scrub when another party of men, Tajurra among them, came out of the scrub carrying bundles of the tumoolu vines. We exchanged "Hellos" and I followed them back over the Crossing and up creek.

Moored there across the creek was the Oonas' long dug-out canoe with Tajalli and three other men sitting in it at equal distances apart. Tajalli nodded to me but kept silent as did the others. In the bottom of the canoe were large stones.

No one spoke, no doubt to avoid frightening the fish that the men knew were in that water below them—deep water that the rocky Crossing holds back like a dam. There was also the possibility that a "'gator" could be lurking down in the depths of that slow-moving creek.

The men with the bundles of tumoolu began crushing and bruising the leaves and vines on a rock away from the water's edge. With that job finished they handed the sap-sticky bundles to the men in the canoe who began tying the bundles to the stones and then quietly let them drop over the side into the water.

The moment the weighted bundles submerged, all the men began chattering and laughing while at the same time watching the surface of the water, for they knew what effect the tumoolu was going to have on the fish lurking below.

For about five minutes nothing happened . . . then a shout from one of the men at the Crossing brought all eyes on to him.

He was brandishing his three-pronged fishing spear with a big fresh-water bream on the end of it. More shouts from the others followed as they began spearing the stunned fish that the creek flow was carrying down to the rocky shallows of the Crossing.

Tajalli and the men hopped out of the canoe and all of us ran back to watch the men at the Crossing as more of the groggily struggling fish came down on the surface of the water.

The catch was a big one—not only of bream but of cat-fish,

a species that must be handled with care because its poisonous spines can cause much pain.

I don't know the reason for the bream making their annual schooling in that stretch of water but the Aborigines know when they are there and make the most of the "Good fella tucker" the annual tumoolu event provides for them.

In the midst of all the shouting and laughter, Tajurra came up to me and said, "You want have good fella tucker longa me tonight, Jimmy, longa camp, longa Oona people?"

"You bet!" I answered eagerly at the prospect of sitting with his people around a communal fire eating fish roasted in the coals.

Then he said, "All Oona women cook this fella fish, women cook 'im fish longa coconut. Tajalli tell me tell you he tell mother belonga me make two big fella coconut and fish inside for Jimmy and Tajurra."

"Gee, thanks," I answered and he picked up two of the still struggling bream. "Give mother belonga you nice fella feed, eh, Jimmy?"

"Yes, thanks." I hooked my two index fingers into the gills of the fish and said, "All right, Tajurra, me come longa camp by and by, have tucker longa you."

He went back to help the men with their catch. I took the fish home to clean for Mum and asked her if I could attend the feast of the tumoolu as the guest of Tajalli at sundown that evening.

My mother's permission was given with her usual admonition: "Yes, provided you get your jobs done around the house first and see to it that the kindling wood is brought into the kitchen for me to light the stove in the morning for breakfast. You do those jobs and you may go to the camp on the understanding that you behave yourself and get home early enough to have a good night's sleep."

"Oh, I will, Mum!" I assured her with just a little pang of

conscience that I was leaving her alone to eat dinner while I had the company of the Oonas and all the fun of the tumoolu feast. But the pang was short-lived because, even if she had been invited to the feast, she would have refused for the simple reason that she had a whole heap of ironing to do from that day's wash.

So I cleaned the two bream for her, did my jobs around the house and headed for the camp as the late afternoon sun was setting.

As I neared the camp I heard the sounds of the Oonas' laughter and revelry, and I smelt the aroma of the cooking of fish and coconuts which made me even more eager for the tumoolu feasting to come.

Tajurra met me and led me into the centre of the camp, which is always reserved for communal events. There I sat down with Tajurra in the space he had kept for us in the circle around the communal fire. I was the only one dressed in navy-blue shorts and shirt. Except for the naked children, everyone else wore the traditional woven bark fibre lap-lap.

The communal fire was about six feet in diameter—a huge circle of glowing charcoal, with a blazing centre-piece of short logs to provide illumination as the overhead tree-tops began to shut out the last failing light of the day.

But it was the women and girls allotted the task of preparing the feast who held my attention. For the past hour or so they must have been hard at it because the ring of glowing coals held scores of green coconuts that the women had filled with fish before placing them in the fire.

All around the circle of the fire the women were still putting the green, fish-filled nuts into the coals. The din of the laughter and chattering going on all around us made it impossible to carry on a conversation with Tajurra, so I just kept on watching as two of the women took a long pole and slipped it through the wire handle of an old four-gallon

kerosene tin filled with water for tea-making. The two
women, one at each end of the pole, lifted the tin and then one
walked around the fire to face the other as they positioned the
tin of water near the blazing centre logs to boil. They placed
the pole on the ground by the fire and one called out to Noola,
Tajurra's mother, who had been holding the woman's baby
while she worked at the fire. Noola returned the baby and
then came to take her allotted family space beside Tajurra and
me. She brought with her a coolamon; this she put on the
ground by the fire. Then she called out to Tajalli and he
came over to us from where he had been sitting with the
elders.

"'Lo, Jimmy," he greeted me. "Soon get real good fella
tucker, eh?"

"'Lo, Tajalli," I answered, grinning. "You bet!"

He then looked round at the now silent circle to make sure
that each family unit was complete. Then he spoke in Oona
which was too rapid for me to follow except for the reference
he made to their god, Oona, the great turtle in the sky, and the
annual feast of the tumoolu and the final command he gave
them to *"Arra tumat bintak!"*—"Begin the feast!"

Immediately every woman representing her family rose
and took her coolamon to the fire and joined the others in
lifting the cooked nuts she selected from the fire. The
contents of the nuts were emptied into the coolamon, and the
empty shells were thrown back into the centre of the fire to
burn and add to the illumination of that scene of tribal peace,
plenty and happiness all around me.

Finally all the families had their coolamons of that creamy
coconut-fish. Noola brought ours and sat down beside Tajalli
to allow the food to cool before we could start in on it, using
our fingers as forks. While we waited we laughed and talked
until a coolamon was passed to us with a pungent green and
brown paste in it. Other coolamons filled with the same

43

concoction were passing among the other families.

Tajalli, Noola and Tajurra looked at me in grinning silence as I inspected the green paste. Then Tajurra said, "This good fella thing, Jimmy. All the same sauce like mother belonga you have longa bottle. Taste 'im."

I did. It tasted like concentrated lime juice with a tangy peppery flavour all its own. I licked my fingers clean and asked, "Where you get 'im?"

Noola laughed and answered, "That fella sauce me make longa green ant, Jimmy."

"Eh?" I answered in disgust at the thought of eating ants. Those green ants are tree-dwelling ants that live in the rain forest scrub and build nests in suitable trees by "stitching" the leaves together. And a more vicious creature than a green ant would be hard to imagine.

But Tajalli's family were not going to delay their feast because of me and my qualms. Noola scooped a lump of the paste from the coolamon and passed it on to her neighbours.

We set to on the fish, each of us scooping up the food with our fingers into our mouths. After a few mouthfuls of the delicious fish, I decided to try a finger-full of the "sauce". I cannot describe the flavour of the cooked coconut-fish with the green-ant "sauce". In much the same manner that a rice pudding is glorified by the addition of nutmeg, so that mixture of fish and coconut was made more delicious by the extra spice of the green ant.

While we were eating, two of the women came back to the fire and lifted off the kerosene tin of boiling water. Then they dropped into the water a pannikin of dry tea and half a billy-can of sugar and lifted the tin back over the fire with their pole to bring the brew to boiling. Then they placed the tin of sweet brewed tea by the side of the fire for everybody to take as they wanted. Noola got her billy full and we sat around sipping in turns from the billy after we had had a second helping of fish.

When all the nuts had been taken from the fire the raw whole fish that were left over from the catch were popped into the softly glowing coals to bake. Amazingly, two or more hours had passed in carefree eating. But by now the children and many of the older people were beginning to nod drowsily. Their bellies were full and it was long past sundown and the time when they were usually asleep in their own mia-mias.

All the women began putting the baked fish into their coolamons and, with fire sticks to light their individual fires as well as to ward off the "debbil-debbils", they began making their way "home" with their men and children following. At least they all had, for the time being, food enough for the morrow's breakfast.

Noola had her cooked fish in her coolamon and with Tajalli she collected her now empty billy-can. They wished Tajurra and me "Goodnight" after Tajalli had collected a blazing fire stick to lead the way home.

Sleepily, Tajurra and I parted, he to go to his own "bedroom"—the long open-fronted thatched shelter at the rear of the camp, reserved for the initiated but unmarried young men of the tribe who share a communal shelter, where already there was a bright fire round which they would sleep.

I watched Tajurra go, and we waved as I turned and walked out of the camp. Once clear of the camp and the trees I glanced over to my left and paused to look at the moon casting a golden pathway over the calm sea. A sudden feeling welled up in me. To myself I whispered, "Please, Oona, never let anything happen to your people to spoil the peace and dignity and happiness which I shared with them this night. Please, Oona, protect them and my mother and me so that we can all live happily here for ever."

The sentimental murmurings of a young lad?—perhaps. But I meant it and still do, as I go on searching for the answer to why we whites cannot live in harmony with the Aboriginal people, regardless of our racial differences and backgrounds.

I turned from looking at the moon and made my way home to the light my mother had left burning for me in my room.

At least I had the promise of a good night's sleep to prepare me for the sudden turnabout of events that were to involve the Aborigines and the Brents in the resolution of a drama that had begun long before my birth.

4

Whatever the day or its significance in the eyes of the Oonas, work on the property had to go on. On the morning after the tumoolu feast my mother said to me, "When you've finished your breakfast, Jimmy, you had better get the weekly rations over to the camp; and, if I'm not mistaken, we'll be needing to get another bullock yarded for slaughtering; there can't be much of the last lot of corned beef left in the brine cask."

"All right, Mum," I answered willingly at the prospect of riding after one of the bullocks if only for the thrill of the rounding up of a suitable beast. "Do you want me to tell Tajalli to take charge of the job?"

"No, not straight away, but you can tell him when you see him that the day after tomorrow will be time enough to get the bullock yarded. Now hurry up and get those rations over to the camp before everybody leaves. Here's the list you'll need."

"Thanks." I took the list, stuffed it in my shirt pocket and, after taking a few crusts of bread to encourage Nellie, our pack-horse, to come to me when I called her, I went on over the rise to the home paddock where I got Nellie's bridle and reins from the saddle-shed.

I had no need to call her because she, the gelding and Creamy came trotting over to the shed the moment they spotted me.

First I made sure to get the bit and bridle on to Nellie before giving her a couple of the crusts. Then I dropped the reins over the hitching rail and was feeding the rest of the crusts to the other two when I saw Tajurra come running over from the camp. He knew, of course, that it was the weekly ration day and was always eager to lend a hand at loading the things on to the big wooden slide parked out at the back of the shed alongside our four-wheeled dray.

"'Lo, Jimmy! You want me help you get rations, eh?"

"You bet!" I agreed, happy at not having to load and unload everything on my own.

We slipped the collar and harness on to Nellie, hooked her up to the slide and set off over the rise and across to the storeroom which was crammed with the stores I needed: one 100 lb sack of flour, one large tin of cream of tartar and soda (baking powder for making the flour into dampers and johnny cakes), one 50 lb bag of sugar, one 6 lb tin of tea, one 50 lb mat of rice, one 7 lb tin of mixed lollies—for the children mainly, one 4 lb block of trade tobacco (the blocks are made up of thin individual small oblong cakes pressed together), half a dozen clay pipes (to replace breakages), one packet of twelve metal boxes of wax (waterproof) matches, a sugar bag full of corned beef (which emptied the storeroom cask), and finally three new quart billy-cans.

All in all it was quite a load of rations we had to manhandle on to the slide, but we eventually got it aboard and set off for the camp. We drove into the camp's centre where all food is dumped for distribution among the families.

We had begun unloading the slide alongside the ashes of the previous night's fire when Guralunni, one of the old women of the tribe, walked past us without speaking. She was shepherding two unusually quiet young girls (Monabi and another girl, Carawul, both about the same age—fifteen). The trio passed on, headed for the rear of the almost empty camp.

I looked at Tajurra for an explanation but he shook his head and nodded in the direction of Tajalli's mia-mia. Tajalli and four of the elders were squatting there in debate about

48

something. Something was afoot but I had to hold my curiosity in check because of Tajurra's warning whisper, "No more talk now, Jimmy. By and by maybe me talk longa you, tell you about pirralulla thing."

I nodded and we went on unloading the slide in silence.

When we had finished he said quietly, "Jimmy, maybe you take 'bacca and pipes longa old men; Tajalli and Trokka no got pipe. Maybe old men tell you about pirralulla thing."

"OK," I answered, knowing that he was trying to avoid having to tell me a tribal secret.

Tajurra would not come with me to present the tobacco and pipes to the men and the message I had for Tajalli. So I left him with Nellie and the slide and went down to the front of the camp where the old men had a small fire burning as a pipe lighter.

The moment I reached the group I sensed the same weird feeling I had had on my previous meeting with them there.

After the usual exchange of friendly greetings I gave Tajalli and Trokka a pipe each and the block of tobacco.

"Ooh!" They both exclaimed in pleasure at getting these unexpected gifts. Tajalli, beaming, told me to "Thank mother belonga you, Jimmy. She good woman all the time look out longa Oona people."

"Yes, me tell her, Tajalli," I assured him and while the men were sharing the tobacco and lighting up their pipes, I glanced up into the palm fronds—sure enough that sinister bone was there, hanging above us by its human-hair cord.

I shuddered even though the temperature must have been near 90 degrees Fahrenheit. When I looked back at the men again I saw a piece of newspaper showing from under a covering of palm leaves beside Trokka—I knew it was the newspaper round the message stick. It had, I knew, been covered when the men had seen me approaching.

I gave Tajalli my mother's message and went back to rejoin

Tajurra. We took the slide back to the saddle-shed and let Nellie go.

When we had taken the harness back into the shed I stopped Tajurra from going out to ask him what the elders were up to under the pandanus palms.

We sat on the table's edge by the door and he asked me if the old men had said anything about why they were holding meetings. I answered they had not.

That seemed to bother him because he did not want to break tribal silence on a matter that did not concern the white people, until I insisted that he should tell me what was going on because I wanted an explanation of the weird feeling that had twice seized me under the pandanus palms. I told him about those two occasions which had left me with a sense of dread that something bad was developing on Oonaderra and, unless he told me what was going on, I would have to ask Tajalli straight out about it.

"No, Jimmy! Please!" he said earnestly. "Suppose Tajalli tell you, all old men punish Tajalli. Suppose he no tell you, he maybe think you make mother belonga you punish 'im—send 'im away longa mission station."

When I pointed out to Tajurra that I had never revealed to others the secrets he had entrusted to me in the past, he relented and said, "All right, Jimmy, suppose me tell you, you no more tell other people about it?"

"Me no more tell anybody about it!" I answered irritably and then added apologetically, "Oh, all right. Me promise— no more tell anybody what you tell me."

And so over the next half hour he explained what he himself understood little about except what he had heard, by listening to the conversations that had been going on between the old men of the tribe.

As he divulged the tribal secret I could clearly see his mounting unease as he told me, "Burunji men come longa

Oonaderra by and by, talk longa Tajalli, talk longa Oona men about other thing."

"What other thing?" I asked.

"That fella talk stick you give 'im old men," he answered. "All the time Tajalli talk longa old Oona men about what that bad fella stick say."

I questioned him further to make him tell me what he had overheard about the message hidden in the carvings on that evil stick. It took quite a bit of persuasion before he weakened. Then, in desperation and fear, he blurted out, "Grandfather belonga you see Burunji man run away when that bad fella man kill woman longa stringybark tree."

Then he told me that my grandfather had also found and helped a mysterious white man who had been with the woman before she died. That white man had been given a horse to ride to Cooktown with Tajalli on another horse leading the way. Then, in a final burst of revelation, Tajurra told me that the Burunji man who had killed the woman was the man who had been entrusted to deliver the message stick to the elders of the Oona tribe. The missing link of what had happened to the stick had been found by me in the old tin trunk, which Tajurra said proved that my grandfather was linked in some way with that mysterious white man and the killing of the woman.

And so the grim story of the meaning of the message stick which was calling for the vengeance of the dolphin god began to unfold, revealing the shocking crimes white men had perpetrated against the Burunji people long ago. I knew now that within the carvings of the message stick I had found in my grandfather's old sea trunk were secrets to which I could only find an answer by the grace and patience of my friend Tajurra.

I asked him what more he had overheard. But all he could tell me was what Tajalli had hinted about the expected arrival of the Burunji men "by and by".

"Burunji men talk trouble longa smoke talk, Tajurra?" I inquired, hoping he could satisfy my curiosity.

"Dunno," he answered. "Tajalli all the time hang 'im bad fella bone longa palm tree because he not like talk to Burunji men about what that stick say."

"What that bone do?" I persisted.

"Me tell you, dunno, Jimmy!" Then in a flash of further irritability at my persistence he said, "That fella bone all the same bone kill man, suppose another man point bone and sing, other man die."

Suddenly he lowered his head in apprehension at what he had allowed himself to reveal about the grim purpose to which that bone on its long human-hair cord could be put—to kill a man by witchcraft.

I patted his shoulder and said, "Don't worry, Tajurra—nobody find out what we talk about. You like come longa house have tea and tucker, eh?"

He brightened up at that, for one of the things he and I loved was having something to eat and drink together in the home of the Brents.

We went on over the rise to the house.

About three that afternoon I walked from the back of the house to the top of the rise and looked across at the cattle yards in the corner of the home paddock. To my surprise, when I looked beyond the yards to the bend in the creek that lies about halfway between the rear of the camp and the Crossing over the creek, I saw that a mia-mia had been erected by the woman and the two girls who had passed us in silence that morning. The woman and girls were still putting finishing touches to the mia-mia outside which a fire was burning.

I was about to return to the house when I saw Trokka and

two of the other elders walking up the track from the camp,
heading for the mia-mia. When they reached it they stood
talking to Guralunni, the old woman in charge of Monabi and
Carawul, the two young girls, who were, as I later learned,
preparing to undergo a ritual called "pirralulla" after sunset
that evening to initiate them into the meaning of womanhood. I turned and went back to the house.

5

The fact that Tajalli was becoming more and more apprehensive about something became more obvious two days later, when the job of yarding and slaughtering the bullock was finished. A good day's work had been accomplished, and on the way back to the house with Tajalli driving the horse and dray, Tajurra and I were in high spirits ... But a peculiar quietness had come over Tajalli, and when we reached the front of the house he left Tajurra and me to look after Nellie and the dray, while he immediately went round to the back steps to talk to Mum. When we joined them, they were chatting and eating apple tart. Mum said, "Tajalli has been telling me how good you two boys have been at helping to get the slaughtering done on time. I must say I'm pleased to hear you've both learned that things get done quickly and well if everybody gives a helping hand."

Tajalli grinned at us. Then suddenly his manner changed. He looked up to the top of the rise anxiously. Then he turned his gaze back to Mum and said, "Me have to hurry, Missus. Thanks for that nice fella tucker ... Bye-bye ..."

The next moment he was running to the top of the rise and disappeared down the other side.

My first impulse was to run after him to find out the reason for his abrupt departure, but Mum stopped me. "Jimmy, and you, Tajurra, finish your tart and take the dray back to the saddle-shed before it gets dark."

"All right, Mum," I answered. We finished our tart and coffee and went through the house, down the front steps, and drove off with Nellie to the saddle-shed.

I walked back towards the camp with Tajurra. To our great surprise, we saw that there were three Oona elders standing, spears in hand, on the track some fifty yards beyond the pirralulla mia-mia at the bend of the creek. Tajalli, still in his khaki clothes, was one of them. He stood a pace ahead of the other two—Trokka and Alitjira, both in lap-laps and headbands. They were looking up the track.

I said to Tajurra, "What for men wait there?"

"Burunji people come, Jimmy," he answered.

"What for he come that way?" I asked, knowing that the circuitous route the Burunjis must have taken to reach Oonaderra was at least twice the distance by way of the coast, direct from their camp at the mouth of a creek away to the north.

Tajurra answered, "Too many big fella river, too many big fella creek, Jimmy; too many sharks, 'gators catch man longa deep water, longa them places."

This made sense, because even my father, whenever he had reason to travel south by horseback, always veered inland away from creek and river mouths so that he could cross the shallower headwaters without the necessity of making the horses swim; a loaded .45 on his hip guaranteed a swift end to any fresh-water crocodiles that might have tried to bail him up on the way.

Tajurra put his finger to his lips to warn me to keep silent.

The time must have been about four o'clock because the shadows were lengthening from the trees silhouetted against the fiery blaze of the sun which was low in the sky.

The seriousness of three Aborigines standing in those lengthening shadows as darkness approached when debbil-debbils and the pantheon of all the other evil spirits known to the Aborigines take over the night world was all too obvious to me. Yet what was even more to be wondered at was that people from another tribe would travel into the evening shadows to keep an appointment on alien tribal territory.

Even I could guess that this most unusual meeting was not entirely concerned with the Oonas' pirralulla ritual of preparing young girls for womanhood. There was something of deadly import to both tribes in the carvings on the message stick which the Oonas now held.

But all my conjecturing was forgotten when Tajurra hissed, "Jimmy. Burunji. Look."

I looked in the direction of his gaze. Away up along the track through the trees were four people, travelling in single file. I could see the spears they were carrying, especially the tall man in the lead. As they came closer I could see they were dressed in lap-laps and headbands; the last figure was a woman carrying a bundle on her head.

Tajalli suddenly stepped forward two paces, drove the point of his spear into the ground and stood in front of it. It was the tribal custom (like the white man's shaking of hands) to assure the others that although the killing spear was within reach, it was not intended for use against anyone who came in search of a peaceful settlement of whatever inter-tribal problem had arisen.

When the oncoming party stopped, they were about four paces from Tajalli. The tall man in the lead drove his spear into the ground and stepped in front of it, just as Tajalli had done. He then spoke to the two men behind him. They at once drove their spears, points down, into the grass verging the track on either side and squatted down behind their standing leader.

The moment that was done, the woman carrying the large bundle on her head walked on past the two groups. We watched her join Guralunni at the pirralulla mia-mia and drop her bundle to squat with her by the fire.

Trokka and Alitjira had also driven their spears into the ground at either side of the track as a token that all was in

56

readiness for the two leaders to talk. They squatted behind Tajalli as the "talk talk" began. It lasted for about ten minutes, and Tajurra fidgeted beside me as the shadows steadily lengthened.

Suddenly Tajalli turned and spoke to Trokka and Alitjira behind him. They got up as the two squatting Burunjis rose to their feet and the two groups, spears in hand, headed for the camp.

Tajurra said to me, "You go home now, Jimmy? Me see you longa morning." Then, like a bat out of hell, he ran for the camp to seek the security of the orange and gold flames of the cooking fires that were beginning to brighten the outlines of the mia-mias and the people moving around them.

It seemed to be a most propitious time for the Burunjis to arrive on Oonaderra on the day of the slaughtering of the bullock. The fresh meat that the women had taken over to the camp for that night's cooking ensured plenty for all. And, of course, there would be plenty of the weekly rations left for tea-making and johnny cakes galore, as well as the tobacco which would be shared generously with the Burunjis in the custom of the Aborigines.

Even at home we had ox-tail soup, a delicacy which my mother and I always enjoyed. The only problem with fresh meat, such as the topside roast and steaks the bullock had provided, was the necessity of partially cooking them ahead of when we would want them. In the tropics, without an ice chest or refrigerator (we had neither at that time), fresh meat goes bad if it is not salted, or par-cooked to preserve it temporarily for twenty-four hours.

But there were other jobs that needed attention, too, such as my going over to the saddle-shed after breakfast the next morning to check the condition of the saddles. I had no sooner reached the shed when I saw Tajurra coming. He did not smile. "What's the matter?" I asked.

He looked at me and answered in a whisper, "Me hear Tajalli talk longa Burunji men, longa Oona old men longa fire, longa night time."

"What for they talk?" I asked.

Then, still in a whisper, he told what he had heard when the elders talked of what had happened all those years ago. He said the Burunji man who had carried the message stick had been sent from the Burunji tribe and had been instructed to get to the Oona elders with it before the mysterious white man and the Burunji woman he was travelling with could reach Oonaderra. Fearfully, Tajurra then told me that part of the message on that carved stick was simple and direct: the Oona men were to intercept the white man and kill him. The woman was not to be harmed.

Then came the next shock: the dead Burunji woman was named Turrapini—Tajalli's sister! She had been initiated in the pirralulla ceremony to become the woman belonging to the leader of the Burunji people—he was the tall man who had led the Burunji party that had been met by Tajalli and his two men on the track the previous day. His name was Kammaluk.

I asked Tajurra why he wouldn't tell me the name of the Burunji man who was roaming the distant ranges, an outcast from his tribe for his killing of Turrapini. Tajurra just said, "Me no more tell 'im name longa that man, Jimmy."

Tajurra would not break the tribal taboo of mentioning a condemned man's name while he still lives; only the leader of the tribe can do that, as a first step to remove the taboo—after the man has paid for his crime—by death.

Even then, in the shed with the bright morning sunshine all around us, I got that queer sensation of the gathering forces that were to be unleashed by the Aborigines through the sorcery they have practised for thousands of years.

Like most white people, I did not want to believe what I could not understand; unlike most white people, I was soon to learn a great deal about Aboriginal sorcery and ritual witchcraft. My lifelong friendship with Tajurra has been the cornerstone of my partial acceptance by the Oona people as a blood-brother of their tribe; hence they trusted me to cooperate in the preservation of their tribal beliefs and customs they follow religiously.

There was nothing more that Tajurra could tell about the real reason for the arrival of the Burunji people except what I myself had worked out—this was a ritual vengeance party; so I said to Tajurra, "Burunji man come longa Oonaderra make trouble, eh?"

"No more make trouble, Jimmy," he answered. "'Im come talk longa Oona old men about plenty other things."

"Maybe about that bad fella talk stick, eh?"

He shrugged non-committally and changed the subject by saying, "Tajalli tell me help you work on saddles."

"All right," I said. "Let's get going!"

For the next hour or so we checked the two lines of saddles slung on their parallel bars running almost the length of the centre of the shed.

With a bottle of neat's-foot oil in one hand and an oil-soaked rag in the other, we oiled the girth-straps and the stirrup leathers, while at the same time we inspected the buckle rivets to make sure they were not beginning to pull out of the leather. We finished the job and went back to the house where Mum was on the veranda, sewing. She brought us lemonade and a plate of brownie. Then she went into the front room to continue with her sewing, leaving Tajurra and me, as she often did, with no parental supervision to cramp our talk.

However, although my mother always cooperated in helping to make my friend and me relaxed and comfortable whenever we were having smoke-o or any other food or refreshments at the house, she also had a firm policy of never allowing us to waste time in prolonged absence from whatever jobs needed doing around the place. She had no patience with excuses for leaving until tomorrow what could be done today.

Twenty minutes or so later, she came on to the veranda and said, "Now, come along you two outlaws and get on with your work."

"OK, Missus," Tajurra answered at once, but I added, "But, Mum, we've done everything we had to do over at the shed—what other job do we have to do now?"

She smiled gently. "If you get me a nice lot of wood in for the stove I might even let you have the day off tomorrow."

"Gee, thanks, Missus," Tajurra piped up. "We get that job done quick smart, eh, Jimmy?"

"You bet! Come on!"

The matter of the firewood was a time-consuming job of harnessing up Nellie to the slide, carting a load of fallen branches from the home paddock over to the house and chopping it up into stove lengths after we had had lunch of cold roast beef and canned vegetables.

It was well into the afternoon before the job was done and I said "So long" to Tajurra as he left to get back to the camp.

I took the slide and Nellie back to the home paddock and let her go with a lump of brownie in her mouth as a reward for her help.

To my surprise, just as I was closing the spring-gate of the paddock to go back to the house, I saw Tajalli running along the top of the rise, waving to me to hold on a while.

I stopped outside the closed gate to watch him, in his lap-lap, as he ran down from the rise to greet me with "Sorry, Jimmy," for stopping me in such a way. Then briefly, in his haste to beat the approaching darkness, he said, "You busy longa morning, Jimmy?"

I told him I would be having the next day off from work and asked what on earth was the matter with him.

He looked anxiously at the westering sun in the distance before he answered, "You like talk longa Burunji men, Jimmy?"

I said, "Yes, I would."

"All right, Jimmy; come longa camp, longa morning. So long."

Before I had time to return his brief farewell, he was gone, running as though hell's demons were after him up and along the top of the rise. I went home, too tired even to mention the incident to Mum.

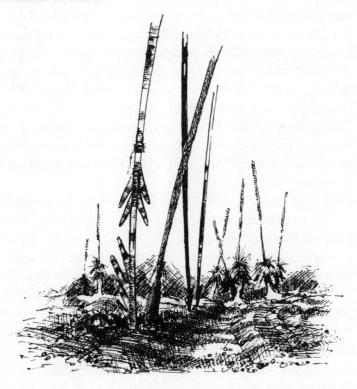

6

To have the day off was indeed a pleasant change from the past few days of having to do all the jobs around the place. It meant that I had no guilty feelings about dodging work to seek fun and games; not that my appointment to meet the Burunji men and the Oona elders would be fun and games—far from it. It was my insatiable curiosity about why the Burunjis wanted to talk to me that had impelled me to accept Tajalli's invitation to be present at the "interrogation" —as it turned out to be.

I arrived at the deserted camp to find the meeting already in progress under the pandanus palms. The men, in lap-laps and headbands, were sitting cross-legged in a circle on the ground. Tajalli and Trokka were sitting together, flanked by four of the Oona elders to form the larger part of the circle. The tall Burunji man who had confronted Tajalli on the track two days previously was flanked by the two men who had arrived with him and they made up the circle with their backs to the sea.

They all looked up at me when Tajalli said, "'Lo, Jimmy."

I returned the greeting and at Tajalli's invitation sat down between him and Trokka.

I again became acutely aware of that peculiar feeling of a brooding something in the atmosphere, even though the bright sea, sky and sunlight were all about us. But a quick glance up into the palm fronds revealed what I had sensed was there—the bone hanging motionless from its human-hair cord.

I hurriedly lowered my gaze to find myself the cynosure of

all the eyes around me. Then Tajalli addressed the tall leader of the Burunjis in rapid Oona (which is similar to the Burunji dialect). The man nodded and Tajalli said to me, "This man, Kammaluk, Jimmy; 'im ask me tell you come longa this place, talk longa that talk stick."

I nodded and Kammaluk said something to Tajalli who, after a slight pause, translated it into pidgin for me and said, "'Im like you, Jimmy; 'im know you all the same brother longa Tajurra. Show 'im mark longa your arm."

I pulled up the short sleeve of my shirt to show the scar on my upper right arm.

Kammaluk leaned forward to stare at the cicatrice and suddenly his stern face relaxed in a broad smile as he pointed at his own arms and chest which bore the tribal marks of cicatrices in the shape of a Z, exactly as I had first seen them on the message stick on the day I found it in my grandfather's trunk. I looked at the other Burunjis and saw the same marks on their arms and chests.

For the assembled Burunjis there was no further need for Tajalli to convince them that "white fella Jimmy" was indeed a blood-brother of the Oona tribe.

During the next ten minutes or so an intense discussion went on between the elders with me silent and ignored by them all until Tajalli raised his right hand and smacked it down on his thigh to bring the group to order and silence. To me he said, "Jimmy, mother belonga you know about that fella talk stick?"

I shook my head. "No, she not know about that talk stick, Tajalli." Which was the beginning of the lies I told to avoid, as I stupidly imagined, the consequences of telling the truth and involving my mother. In my stupidity I failed to remember that my mother was already showing symptoms of a sickness which had stricken her soon after she had seen that evil message stick when I had put it on the kitchen table

63

during her bread-baking.

It was obvious that the elders were deeply concerned about my mother and what would inevitably happen to her if she had seen the message stick.

They accepted my bare-faced lie without comment.

Kammaluk then spoke rapidly to Tajalli, making several references, obviously of approval, to "white fella Jimmy", three words of English he had learned, no doubt, from Tajalli and the Oona elders during his stay in the camp.

Tajalli translated Kammaluk's remarks to me by saying, "Burunji men ask you keep quiet longa mother belonga you. By and by that fella stick come back longa house belonga you. Burunji man no more want keep 'im stick when 'im catch bad fella man by and by."

I assured him that I had no intention of ever saying anything at all to my mother about the message stick. I kept to myself the fact that I knew the "bad fella man" was the Burunji man who had killed Turrapini, Tajalli's sister.

After this, Tajalli and the others began a criss-cross of rapid talk which was too fast for me to follow. The discussion went on for about fifteen minutes; then Tajalli again raised his hand and brought his palm down sharply on his thigh. The men fell silent. Turning to me he said, "Long time ago Burunji man kill sister belonga me, longa up there." He swivelled around from his cross-legged position to point in the direction of Cannon Ball Rock.

"What for?" I asked.

He then told me that a Burunji man had been sent by the Burunji elders to deliver the talk stick to the Oona elders to tell them to kill a white man who had stolen Kammaluk's woman, Turrapini. "Turrapini", Tajalli went on, "see talk stick that man carry; 'im kill sister belonga me."

He explained that for a woman to see such a stick meant that she would die either by violence or by a slow, lingering

64

death because of the debbil-debbil of death that dwelt in the stick's secret taboo carvings. I dared not show the terror I felt when I realized what this meant to my mother.

And so Tajalli began to recount the events of the past to me under the watchful eyes of the assembled elders. He went on to explain that the white man named on the talk stick had been responsible for the deaths of many of the Burunji tribe and of several white men too.

He then told how the whole shocking story began. Pointing north to the tip of Cape York he said a boat had come from the direction of Torres Strait with four white men on board. The boat anchored in the lee of a tiny uninhabited island that directly faces the Burunji tribe's camp at the mouth of a fresh-water creek on the mainland. That night the men rowed over to the camp with demijohns of rum and other grog. The novelty of the white men bringing the grog was welcomed by some of the Burunjis. The resulting drunkenness of the Burunjis and the white men led to the beginning of an orgy with the white men lusting after the young girls of the tribe and trying to catch them.

Then Tajalli began the dreadful account of what took place when the whites could not catch the Burunji girls, who naturally fled the camp and went bush with others of their people. As their leader, Kammaluk had taken charge of the girls and the others who waited until the white men, tired of their stay there, would go back to their boat and leave the Burunjis in peace.

The white men did return to their boat the next morning, but when Kammaluk led his people out of the bush back into the camp they found a Burunji man and his woman lying dead where they had been clubbed to death with a nulla-nulla. The reason for the killings was not far away. In the dead couple's mia-mia Kammaluk found the body of a white man who had obviously been speared to death by the

Aboriginal man before he and his woman died defending themselves against one of the other drunken intruders.

The tracks of the white men all around the mia-mia, Tajalli explained to me, were conclusive proof to the Aborigines that the other white men had killed the Burunji man and his woman.

"Other white men go away longa boat, Tajalli?" I asked him.

"No, Jimmy; by and by white men come back longa Burunji camp, bring 'im big fella turtle for Burunji people."

"What for?" I again asked, when Tajalli appeared reluctant to tell me why the white men had brought the turtle they had caught and killed over on the island.

After a short conversation with Kammaluk, who finally nodded his agreement, Tajalli told me what happened next.

As soon as Kammaluk saw the white men rowing across from the anchored boat, he ordered his people to leave the camp with him again and to watch from the surrounding bush to see what the white men were up to. The white men stepped out of the dinghy in the shallow water near the beach facing the camp and then carried a dead turtle from the dinghy up to the front of the camp. Their leader then called out to the watching Burunjis, expressing their repentance for their behaviour the night before, and explaining that the turtle was a gift of food for the Burunjis as a token of the white men's sorrow over what had happened.

As further token of their "good intentions" the white men went back to the dinghy and returned to their boat.

As Tajalli explained to me, the Burunjis, unable to go about their usual hunting and gathering of food since the arrival of the white men, had accepted the gift gratefully. Hunger hastened their eagerness to get the turtle on to a blazing fire, on its back so that its carapace could make a caldron.

It was easy to imagine what followed when the turtle was cooked and dragged from the coals to let the Burunjis dip into the juicy contents of the turtle's shell to satisfy their hunger ... Too late ... by the time the first of the people had swallowed a few mouthfuls of the meat it was too late for them to realize that the turtle had been dosed with poison, which, from Tajalli's description of its convulsive effects on the eaters, must have been strychnine.

Tajalli's grim-faced account of that horrible act of multiple homicide wrought by the white men on the naive Burunjis brought back to me that awful feeling of nameless fear I had already experienced twice before.

I hoped that the terrible story was at an end, but it wasn't, because Tajalli was interrupted by Kammaluk raising *his* right hand to bring it down smartly on his thigh to halt the story.

Kammaluk began to speak to the two Burunji men on either side of him. As he addressed each in turn, obviously putting something to them for their approval, they cast searching looks at me. Their final *"Sibba! Sibba!"* ended the talk; Kammaluk nodded to Tajalli, who turned to look at me before he asked, "You want me tell you about other thing white men do, Jimmy?"

I nodded, even though not really wanting to hear more because I'd had nightmares aplenty before, when Tajurra had transmitted to me his own fear of what was contained in the deadly witchcraft of that Burunji message stick. Now I was listening to something far more terrible than my mind could handle. But the meeting of the Burunjis and the Oonas had been called for that very reason; and so Tajalli told me of the next happening in that massacre of blacks and whites.

He told me how Kammaluk had made his people take their dead and put them into hollow trees (that is the Burunji custom in the "burial" of their dead). The body of the white

67

man, his fellow whites apparently having no further interest in him, was taken into the deep bush and buried under a cairn of heavy rocks where no one was ever likely to come across it because the Aboriginal tracks are designed to lead *away* from such places on which a tribal taboo has been placed. That cairn therefore remains untouched, unseen, to this very day.

Thus, to continue Tajalli's account: the Burunjis returned to their camp at sundown believing that they would be safe under the protection of darkness. But once again they underestimated the cunning of the three remaining white men, who no doubt were watching from their boat. They would, of course, have seen the ritual fire that Kammaluk and the elders lit to carry out their corroboree of lament for the dead who they believed were journeying back to the Dreamtime—the Valhalla of all Aborigines after their sojourn on earth, and, in the case of the Burunjis, under the protective aegis of the great dolphin in the sky.

While Kammaluk and the elders were carrying out their ritual corroboree they were totally unaware of the three armed white men, who rowed ashore in the darkness and crept up to the edge of the firelight. They watched the tribal elders sitting in a circle while Kammaluk was in the act of casting the sacred contents of his woven human-hair bag on to the ground in front of him. As the sacred objects fell from the bag the elders scrutinized the pattern they made to see what it foretold.

According to Tajalli, Kammaluk was scooping the sacred objects back into the bag when the white men caught sight of the most sacred of them all ... a glistening black pearl—shaped like, but bigger than, a pigeon's egg!

There was a sudden rush as the white men came crashing out of the darkness into the red glare of the firelight; but Kammaluk was quick enough to somersault backwards, still clutching the bag and its precious contents. The leader of the white men raised his rifle and fired.

The bullet hit Kammaluk in the shoulder. There was then a grappling skirmish with the elders who disarmed the white men and made them lie face down on the ground. Kammaluk leapt back into the firelight to prevent the elders from clubbing the white men to death.

At this point in his story Tajalli spoke to Kammaluk who nodded and swung round to reveal the two white scars where the bullet had struck him in the left shoulder and ploughed through the flesh to emerge near his arm-pit. Those two scars could only have been made by a .32 calibre rifle bullet entering and leaving the wound.

Kammaluk turned back to face Tajalli and me again. I said to Tajalli, "What Burunji men do longa white men—kill 'im?"

"No more kill 'im, Jimmy. White fella leader kill other two white men."

"How?" I asked again.

Instead of answering me directly, Tajalli told me that the Burunjis had held the white men prisoners for two days, trying to decide what to do with them. Kammaluk knew that if the white men were to reach a white settlement, their version of the happenings at the Burunji camp would be believed and Kammaluk's people would have to face the dire consequences of a punitive expedition by the police.

But on the second day the appeal that the Burunji elders had made to the great dolphin in the sky, to rid them of the white men, was answered. At daybreak on the second day the white men were held prisoner a cyclone roared in over the Coral Sea. All that day the wind screamed and the rain fell in an endless avalanche, sweeping away the entire camp. The Burunjis were left with only their meagre possessions and the three prisoners shivering in the debris of what had been the mia-mia where they were guarded by three Burunjis armed with ten-foot-long killing spears. That day merged into night with the roaring wind and rain unabated, until the "piccaninny daylight" came and the wind dropped. Over the next few days the weather cleared before the Wet Season began with its deluges of rain and floods that continued for weeks on end.

But out on the grey heaving sea only the island showed as a blur on the horizon ... the boat of the white men had vanished beneath the waves, and their dinghy was found smashed to matchwood on the beach.

The destruction of the camp meant little to the Burunjis, Tajalli explained, because the onset of the Wet Season was also the time of their annual Walkabout. At this time, too, the initiation of the young men of the tribe into manhood had to be performed on the circuit of their traditional tribal food areas of water lily bulbs, aquatic birds and barramundi on the billabongs, lagoons and swamps filled by the rains of the Wet Season.

With the boat and the dinghy gone, Tajalli said, the Burunjis only had to get rid of the white men to prevent them getting back to civilization to tell *their* story.

"But you tell me Burunji people no more kill 'im white men, Tajalli," I argued.

"'Im no more kill white men, Jimmy," he answered, in such a way that I knew he was telling the truth. "'Im make white men get lost longa Gumrai-Gumrai."

"Gumrai-Gumrai?" I asked, puzzled by the Aboriginal word, which he explained meant "Big fella swamp, Jimmy."

And then came Tajalli's account of what the Burunjis, under Kammaluk's leadership, planned to do with the white men. The Burunji men, women and children were ordered to start on the Walkabout immediately. They left Kammaluk, three of the elders and four young men who were to undergo the ceremony of initiation into manhood at a secret hideout in the distant ranges. In addition three fully initiated men were assigned to guard the white men who were to be released in the Gumrai-Gumrai. The Burunjis believed they would never find their way out of its labyrinths of swamp grass, knee-deep water and ooze, stretching for miles in every direction. And there was one final requirement—two initiated, strong young Burunji women were to go with the party to do the cooking for the men; one of those young women was Kammaluk's woman—Turrapini—Tajalli's sister.

Tajalli went on to tell me that the main party of Burunji men, women and children set off to travel north to make the circuit into the ranges, a two-day journey, and there they were to camp and wait for Kammaluk's initiation party to meet up with them in the late afternoon of the day after the initiation rituals had been carried out. As soon as the main party had left, Tajalli said, Kammaluk led his party and the captive white men west towards the dreaded Gumrai-Gumrai, the crossing of which is part of the initiation ordeal of the young men.

As a final and foolish precaution, according to Tajalli, Kammaluk had ordered the three white men's rifles to be taken along to be hidden at the hideout to make sure that they were well away from where any police patrol might find them. They were wrapped and tied together with bark and carried by one of the men in charge of the prisoners. Kammaluk was in the lead, carrying in his left hand his ceremonial shield with their god Burunji painted on it in white ochre. Around his neck, hanging by its human-hair cord, was the bag containing the sacred Burunji objects. Like the other initiated men and the elders, and despite the bullet wound in his shoulder, he carried a long killing spear in his right hand.

The two women brought up the rear, carrying the things

71

they needed for cooking, which was a simple enough matter on dry land but not when they entered the Gumrai-Gumrai on the second day and had to travel through the knee-deep swamp.

Tajalli paused in his telling of the story to ask Kammaluk something about that second day. Tajalli listened, nodded and said to me, "Kammaluk let white men go longa swamp before that big fella swamp finish longa ranges. White men cry, talk plenty but Kammaluk leave 'im there, go on before dark come."

In the account of what happened next, Tajalli told me Kammaluk believed that the approaching darkness would stop the three men from following because he had picked a point where high swamp grass barred the view of the ranges a mile or so ahead. Tajalli said he should have released the three in the middle of the swamp but he hadn't because he had thought the men might have found their way back the way they had come.

He said Kammaluk had told him that the swamp grass swallowed up the party and so he felt safe from being followed. Before darkness fell Kammaluk's party had reached dry ground and, happily, several of the group had caught enough tortoises and a couple of file snakes in the swamp to warrant a fire for the women to cook them.

That fire, as was the case back at the camp, led to the Burunjis' undoing, although not immediately. The women cooked the file snakes in their skins in the coals of the fire with the tortoises cooking in their shells alongside them. After the meal the Burunjis slept round the fire.

At sun-up the next morning Kammaluk ordered the men of the party into the hideout in the almost perpendicular face of the black basalt cliff that stretched north and south for miles along the edge of the swamp. The women were left to gather whatever food they could in the vicinity, while the men and boys followed Kammaluk in a frightening climb up the face of the cliff to an almost invisible entrance about halfway to the top. The ramparts towered almost a hundred and fifty feet above and were surmounted by a mantle of dense scrub. Tajalli explained how, one by one, the boys were sent to climb up into the cleft. Then Kammaluk, his bag of sacred objects hanging from his neck by its human-hair cord, ordered the men on the cliff face below to begin handing up to him the sacred shield, a bundle of plaited grass torches, and then a firestick to light them. Then, Tajalli said, the men all disappeared into the cleft, leaving Turrapini and the other woman to keep the fire going for the cooking of more tortoises the men had caught that morning for the meal they would have on their return.

The men's spears, as well as the rifles wrapped and tied up in bark, had been left near the cooking fire, which was another mistake Kammaluk had made in his assumption that the white men would never find their way out of the swamp. They did.

All unsuspecting, the women went about their work. They were taken completely by surprise when the white men suddenly emerged from the swamp and grabbed them.

At that juncture in Tajalli's narrative, Kammaluk interrupted him and they both engaged in another rapid discussion with the others which ended in a *"Sibba! Sibba!"* of agreement from Tajalli. He then translated for me what the meeting had decided to do: the Burunjis were to return to Burunji territory and prepare for a secret corroboree at the very place in the Gumrai-Gumrai swamp which Tajalli had just been describing.

When I asked what was the purpose of the corroboree, Tajalli explained that, because of what had happened on that day when the white men had seized the Aboriginal women, a curse had been laid on the secret inner cave where the initiation rituals were carried out. I was made to understand that no more could be revealed to me until the night on which the corroboree was to be held to lift the curse. And, Tajalli said, the elders had decided to ask me to witness the secret ceremony of lifting the curse and the setting in motion of their plan to catch the outcast Burunji man, a wandering fugitive hiding in the ranges from the vengeance of his tribe.

Suddenly the ringing of an old cow-bell by my mother summoning me home ended the meeting for me. I stood up, cupped my hands to my mouth and gave a "Coo-ee" to let her know I was on my way. But Tajalli, from his cross-legged posture, stopped me. "Wait, Jimmy."

I paused and he said, "Jimmy, you no more talk longa mother belonga you about that bad fella talk stick, eh?"

Without a moment's hesitation I answered, "No, Tajalli, me no talk longa her about that talk stick."

With that reassurance, Tajalli said Kammaluk was going to keep the talk stick and that I would get it back after the corroboree.

I didn't care for that, but under the circumstances there was little I could do about it, and, in any case, I had to get home . . .

Tajalli's parting words were, "Me come longa house see mother belonga you, tell about you find talk stick."

I nodded and ran for home to avoid causing myself any further trouble.

7

My mother's first reaction on my walking up the back steps was, "Well, well, so the prodigal returns. And where might you have been without telling me where you were going before you left so suddenly this morning?"

"Sorry, Mum," I apologized. "I've been over at the camp talking to Tajalli and some Aborigines who came down from the north two days ago."

"Oh, and what's so important about a few Aborigines paying a friendly visit on Oonaderra, might I ask?"

"Well, I don't think they came all the way from the north just to pay a casual visit, Mum. They came on Tajalli's invitation when he talked with them a few days ago by smoke signals on the beach."

"Oh, and how do you know he did that?"

"Because I saw old Trokka with Tajalli when he was sending the signals when I was on the *Curlew* the other day."

I was trying, of course, to get around to telling her that I had been the cause of the signals being sent, so I said, "Remember that funny carved stick I found in Grand-dad's old trunk?"

"No, what funny carved stick? . . . Oh, yes; but I was too busy baking bread to pay much attention to it. Why?"

"Well, Mum, I'm sorry, but I took it over to the camp the other day to show Tajalli and the old men. Tajalli has kept it, and he wants to keep it for the time being."

She laughed. "Well, so long as he brings it back when he's done with it, I'm sure no harm will be done. Its only value, as far as I'm concerned, is that it belonged to your grandfather

75

and should be kept in the trunk because of its association with him. After all, it must have been in there for at least twenty-six years, seeing that your grandfather died in nineteen-twenty, long before you were born, or were even thought of. And another thing, young fellow me lad—don't you ever again go taking things out of this house without my permission, or else."

"I won't, Mum," I promised, and meant it.

"Well, then," she said, "we'll say no more about it; just make sure you tell Tajalli I want the silly thing back again. Do you understand?"

"Yes; but there is more to be said about it, Mum," I told her. "Tajalli's coming over to speak to you about it; he told me to tell you he would be coming over by and by."

"All right, then, we'll hear what he has to say when he gets here. Is that all?"

"No, Mum—there is one other thing."

"Well, don't just stand there hesitating, let's hear it!"

"Will you promise not to tell Tajalli that you know anything about that carved stick, please?"

"Now, look here," she answered in exasperation at my dilly-dallying around the subject. "What on earth has my seeing that stupid stick got to do with Tajalli, or anybody else for that matter?"

"A lot," I answered and tried to explain that the Aborigines don't like the women seeing secret objects such as that carved stick, because they believe that some things are taboo to women. "Please don't tell Tajalli, Mum," I pleaded. "Just tell him, if he asks you, that you don't know anything about it."

She looked searchingly at me for a moment or two before she answered, "Very well, then, if I must tell a white lie to protect you, I will, on the understanding that some good will come of it for all concerned."

76

"Gee, thanks, Mum," I answered, relieved *for the time being* that I had averted whatever evil consequences were inherent in the message stick being seen by a woman.

She got up and said, "Well, how about we have lunch now, eh?"

"Good-o!" I agreed, and followed her into the kitchen to give a hand.

Much later when we were back on the veranda, sitting at the table, Tajalli suddenly appeared at the back steps dressed in his khaki rig-out to greet us with "G'day, Missus, Jimmy."

We answered his greeting and Mum said, "Sit down, Tajalli, and make yourself comfortable."

"Thanks, Missus." He smiled, in an embarrassed sort of way, and sat himself down on the top step to face us. He put his hat on his knees.

Mum said, "Jimmy tell me, Tajalli, about you come longa house, see me, talk longa me about something."

"Yes, Missus, Jimmy find stick belonga my people."

Relief! He believed I had told the truth about her not having seen it. He just said quietly, "You like me tell you about that fella stick, Missus?"

"Yes, of course," she answered, to encourage him to go on. In that quietly deferential manner of the Aboriginal when he is respectfully asked anything by white people, he began. "Long time ago people longa Burunji tribe send that fella stick to tell Oona old men about white man make trouble longa Burunji people."

"What sort of trouble, Tajalli?" she asked.

He shrugged and spread out his hands, palms upwards to indicate he didn't want to go into details. "This white man bad fella, make trouble longa Burunji people all the time. By and by white man steal Burunji woman, make her take 'im longa scrub, show 'im way longa Oonaderra; Burunji people get big fella fright, think white man tell police lies about

77

Burunjis; make policeman come, make more big fella trouble longa Burunji people . . ."

"Who this man, Tajalli?" she asked when he paused to consider what more he should say. He just shrugged again and answered, "Dunno name belonga 'im, Missus. Policeman not know name belonga 'im. Grandfather belonga Jimmy not know name."

"How you know about white man?" she then asked.

"Grandfather belonga Jimmy give that bad fella white man horse, give me horse, tell me take white man longa Cooktown see doctor."

"You mean you take that white man longa Cooktown, Tajalli?"

He nodded and went on, "Grandfather give me letter take longa doctor, longa Cooktown. By and by me bring horses back longa Oonaderra, leave white man longa Cooktown, very sick."

"Oh, what that man get sick for?" she asked.

Tajalli scratched his head in perplexity. Then he said, haltingly, "White man get bad eyes; shake all the time, talk mad talk; got fever belonga scrub."

In an instant Mum gave the probable answer for the white man's shakes and delirium symptoms. "Scrub fever, Tajalli?" she suggested and he nodded. But the question of the white man's "bad eyes" was left unanswered.

Mum next asked him who the Aboriginal woman was the white man had stolen.

"She Turrapini," he answered. "Sister belonga me."

"Oh," Mum answered. "What happened to her?"

"Burunji man kill her," Tajalli answered.

"Oh, my God!" she exclaimed. "What for?"

"Dunno, Missus. Oona people find body, put 'im longa tree longa that way . . ." He pointed vaguely in the direction of the ranges, no doubt to avoid telling her exactly where the

78

body was hidden.

"What for you no more put body longa other dead people belonga Oonas, Tajalli?" she inquired sympathetically.

"No can do that, Missus," he answered. "Too many debbil-debbils watch that tree. By and by we catch Burunji man who kill 'er, and we make big fella corroboree tell debbil-debbils go away."

Fortunately, Mum had the good sense not to ask him who that Burunji man was who had murdered his sister, because, in her capacity as a cattle station owner, she would have been bound by law to inform the police if she knew his name (if he were still alive). But she did discreetly avoid any involvement in an event that happened long before she arrived on Oonaderra, by saying, "Well, Tajalli, maybe that Burunji man dead now, eh?"

He glanced sharply at me to let me know he was agreeing with her when he said to her, "Yes, Missus, maybe 'im dead now." That look was familiar to me, because of my long association with the Aborigines, and I knew their silent method of conveying a confidence by a sharp glance at a fellow Aborigine when they wish not to be contradicted on a strictly tribal matter.

But I was totally unprepared for his next statement when he said to Mum, "Burunji men ask me to go longa Burunji people, take Jimmy longa me, too."

"Eh? What!" she exclaimed in horror at the suggestion that I go with him. "What on earth you want take Jimmy for, Tajalli?" she asked.

"Burunji men like Jimmy, Missus," he answered, and then grinned when he said, "Burunji men like red hair belonga Jimmy."

"Why?" was all she could say to that. She had always maintained my hair was too red for a boy, especially me, the first of the Brents ever to have it.

Tajalli grinned again and said, "All myall Aborigines long time ago, say red hair belonga god come down longa ground from Dreamtime longa sky. Burunji men say ask me ask you let Jimmy go longa Burunji camp, help Burunji people go back longa place belonga them; make big fella corroboree; make everybody happy; no more trouble come then, Missus. We come back longa Oonaderra, make everybody happy longa Oona people, too."

He watched her anxiously as she thought about his proposal. Then turning to look at me she said sternly, "Jimmy, did you know that Tajalli was going to ask me to let you go with him to the Burunji camp?"

"No! Truly I didn't, Mum," I answered, as much taken aback by her thinking that of me as I was over her temporary doubting of Tajalli's sincerity.

She quickly recovered herself, however, to say to Tajalli, "No more take horses, Tajalli; too poor, too skinny go long way. How far this Burunji camp?"

With a circular sweeping motion of his hand he indicated the long round-about way west and north and then east we would have to go to reach the camp, "Longa creek, longa sea, all the same Oonaderra, Missus. Suppose we walk, take maybe three, four day get there."

On an impulse, I chipped in with, "Hey, Mum, how about we go by boat, the *Curlew*, eh?"

"Eh, nothing!" she retorted. "Who, might I ask, will take charge of the *Curlew*?"

"Me, Mum. Haven't I handled her all the way from Cairns and back at least twice since you taught me how to handle the engine and how to steer by landmarks along the coast?"

"Well, yes," she agreed, and my heart leapt because I knew she was weakening.

But before she would commit herself she said to Tajalli, "You know about where deep water belonga reef go longa

Burunji camp?" As she spoke she pointed to the sea northward.

Tajalli nodded eagerly and said, "Too right, Missus, me go longa Burunji camp longa canoe plenty times; how 'im deep water longa reef all the way."

"All right then, suppose me let Jimmy take boat, you talk longa 'im all the same father—make 'im do proper thing, all the time, keep boat longa deep water."

"Too right, Missus!"

Before she could say any more I burst in with, "Hey, Mum, what about Tajurra? He knows how to handle the *Curlew*; remember last week I let him take her through the channel and back when we made that run with you on board to give the engine plenty of time to charge the batteries? Remember?"

"Yes, yes, I remember. And I suppose Tajalli won't mind taking charge of the pair of you."

For a moment I thought she was going to cry because she brushed her hand over her eyes, but then she excused herself and hurried into the house on the pretext that she needed to look at the barometer there. She was having another turn.

Tajalli looked at me in consternation to ask, "What for mother belonga you get sick, Jimmy?"

"Oh, she all right," I assured him. "She get little bit sorry we go away longa boat. By and by she be all right."

And so she appeared to be when she returned a few minutes later and resumed her place at the table with me. Tajalli immediately said to her, "No more worry about Jimmy, about Tajurra, Missus; that two fella not plurry fools; me make 'im do proper thing all the time longa boat."

"I'm sure you will," she answered. "But more better we pull 'im boat up longa beach, look longa bottom, clean 'im barnacle off."

He didn't know what she meant by "barnacle" but he knew

that the boat's hull must be scraped clean down to the copper sheathing that protects her planking against the teredo wood worm, or ship worm, which would soon ruin her timbers if it got in through a crack or break in that sheathing.

He said, "All right, Missus, we pull boat up longa beach now—tide come in now." He looked over at the camp. The Oona hunting and fishing parties were returning and we could see them moving around the camp. He put his hat back on, stood up and gave the swamp pheasant call of "Woop, woop, woop, woop, w-o-o-o-o-o-p."

An answering call came back immediately and a party of Oona men came running across to the house.

While he was waiting for them he said to Mum, "You like come down see men pull boat up longa beach, Missus?"

"Yes, Tajalli."

He nodded and ran around to the front with Mum and me following him. He waved to the men to come on down to the beach and we all went there together.

It made no difference to Mum that the dozen or more Oona men who came swarming down on the beach were all dressed in their lap-laps. She seemed to enjoy their laughter and shouting when Tajalli told them what he wanted them to do.

Once we had the boat safely beached we went round to the port side to inspect the hull. My mother's decision to check the hull was timely indeed—the barnacles were massed thick from keel to water-line, and the clicking, sucking sound they made was new to me.

At that stage of the work, Mum was able to come and inspect the hull without getting her feet wet. She looked in amazement at the massed barnacles and said to Tajalli, "We no got tools; how we clean boat?"

He laughed. "No more worry, Missus. Me fix 'im." He spoke to the men who then ran back to the creek bank in front of the camp and returned each with a "kroob"—an oval flat stone about six inches wide and a foot long. Behind the men came six Oona women carrying coolamons and walking at a leisurely pace.

Under Tajalli's supervision the men began striking the stones on the shaft of the anchor to break them in half into two chisel-pointed tools. By that time the women had arrived and, as the men began to chisel the barnacles off the copper sheathing, the women collected the shellfish in their coolamons, everybody laughing and chattering away happily at the prospect of barnacles as a tasty addition to that evening's meal.

At last the port side was scraped clean down to the sheathing, which glowed bright in the late afternoon sunglow . . . Not a blemish or a fault in the copper could be seen. Mum was very happy and so, too, was Tajalli, who said, "We wait for tide all same this one, longa morrow, Missus."

"You no more do 'im other side longa morning, Tajalli?" she asked.

He shook his head. "Only little fella tide longa morning," he explained. "No more come up longa boat, Missus."

It was true; at that time of the year the daily tides alternate, with a big high tide in the afternoon and a lesser high tide in the morning. It meant that no more work could be done on the *Curlew* till late the following evening.

Mum nodded and said, "Well, it's getting late, so we had all better get home to dinner. Come along, Jimmy, get your boots and come and help me light the kitchen stove." She thanked Tajalli and the others and we all left the beach; the Oonas, of course, were more than willing to get back to their camp before night closed in around them.

In consideration of the fact that my previous "day off" had been cancelled out by other matters, my mother allowed me, the following morning after breakfast, to have the day to myself, provided that I made myself helpful to Tajalli and the other men when the afternoon's high tide came in to float the *Curlew*. I promised I would and she let me slip over to the camp.

When I got halfway there, I saw that the whole tribe of the Oonas had assembled in front of the pirralulla mia-mia at the bend of the creek, so I crossed over there in time to see Monabi and Carawul standing outside the mia-mia with the Burunji woman behind them. Trokka came out from behind the mia-mia carrying two coolamons, two yam-sticks and two of the new billy-cans I had taken to the camp with the Oonas' weekly rations. He placed one billy-can and a yam-stick into each coolamon and handed one to each young woman. Then he stepped back into the assembled people, who parted to form a passageway through them.

The Burunji woman stooped, picked up the bundle she had brought with her, and then spoke to the two young women, who nodded and fell into step behind her as she led the way through the people.

I glanced up along the track, and there, waiting some fifty or so yards away, were Kammaluk and the other two Burunji men. He waved his spear for the three women to come, turned and with the two men behind him set off at a rapid pace. The three women hurried to catch up with them.

Until then not a word had been spoken by anyone, but suddenly a babble of talk broke out as the Oonas separated into groups to go about their daily food gathering. For a moment or so I thought I was going to be left alone, until Tajurra came up behind me with a "'Lo, Jimmy."

"G'day, Tajurra," I answered in relief at the sight of him, grinning and as happy as I was that we were together again. "Tajalli tell you we go longa boat, longa Burunji people?" I asked him.

He grinned wider than ever and told me his father had told

him everything about the journey north into Burunji territory.

Then I asked him if he knew how the two young women felt about having to leave the Oona camp to live with the Burunjis. He just smiled and said, "Last night everybody have little fella corroboree longa camp where we have tumoolu tucker longa fire before." He told me the two young women had been there with their parents.

While we were talking I noticed he kept looking down along the track that leads along the fringe of trees skirting the camp down to the beach. Soon the reason for his watching became apparent: dressed in their lap-laps and headbands came Tajalli and Trokka, the old man carrying something small in both hands held in front of him. Tajurra whispered to me to follow him away from the deserted mia-mia. We walked across to the tree in front of the cattle yards. We watched the two men walk to the mia-mia and kneel down at the right side of its low opening. Then Tajalli took from his neck the woven human-hair bag containing the Oonas' sacred objects and put it on the ground in front of him.

Both men then began to swing their hands in circular movements as they faced each other, at the same time bending and raising their heads in what can only be described as a mimicry of something vaguely familiar to me. I looked at Tajurra for an explanation. He said, "They talk longa Burunji."

"Burunji?" I replied in astonishment. "No more Burunji people here!"

He shook his head and said, "Burunji big fella fish all the same god longa Burunji people."

Of course! I had completely forgotten that the totem of the Burunjis is the dolphin. He could not, however, tell me what the two men were doing, or what it had to do with the dolphin.

85

He motioned me to follow him away and said, "Tajalli maybe get mad longa me stand here longa you. More better we go away. We go longa house, eh?"

"All right," I answered and over to the house we went. In the kitchen Mum was making out a list of the things we would need on the journey north. Her suggestion that "If you two care to help me get this list worked out and checked, then I would be a very grateful mother," got an immediate response from us, especially Tajurra, who said, "Too right, me help you all the time now." And so we both hopped in to help her throughout the day to get everything organized.

The big tide came in that afternoon almost an hour later than the day before. Tajalli, of course, knew this and therefore had his men and the women ready for a prompt start on the careening of the barnacles from the starboard side; that side was cleaned down to the copper sheathing and everything was found to be intact and in good condition.

Another gathering of the barnacles by the women got them as good a quantity as the day before. But the later tide allowed no time for lingering after the job was done; the Oonas hurried away to the camp, leaving Mum and me with a "Bye-bye, Missus; bye-bye, Jimmy." We went on home.

To save time and the necessity of rowing out to the *Curlew* with the provisions for the journey, Mum decided to load everything into the boat while she was beached. Stores, water, drums of fuel, even a bottle of citronella were all loaded aboard the next day direct from the dray when Nellie hauled it down to the beach alongside the *Curlew*. Tajalli, Tajurra and I stowed the load aboard.

Our provisions did not include a rifle and ammunition for me. By some mutual arrangement between Mum and Tajalli, I had been told the previous night by my mother that I was not to take any sort of fire-arm with me on the trip. No amount of talking on my part would move her to let me take a rifle. Her firm "No, Jimmy, no rifle, and that's final," had warned me not to persist further.

A last-minute check by Mum of everything, even down to the fire extinguishers in the galley and over the engine cowling, satisfied her that all was well. Then a problem arose that seemed insurmountable: the tide to float the boat would be another hour later, and would not reach the *Curlew* before darkness set in, when all the Oonas prefer to be back by their fires in the safety of the camp. Furthermore, to have left the boat there unattended on the rising big tide would have meant getting her swamped before the tide could lift her on to an even keel.

Mum was anxiously waiting on the beach with Tajalli and the men he had brought along for the re-floating, but the oncoming darkness made it all too obvious that the tide would not float the *Curlew* before night set in.

Suddenly Tajalli called out to Mum, who was standing up near the bow anchor, "Missus, you get light belonga lamp? You get two fella lamps, we stay, fix up boat, eh?"

"Yes, yes, Tajalli," she answered. Then she called out to me, "Jimmy, run up to the house and light a couple of the hurricane lamps and fetch them back. Oh, and you can light the kitchen lamp, too, while you're at it. Hurry now!"

"O K, Mum." I raced up the bank and across to the house. By the time I got the lamps lit and back to the beach, Tajalli had the men building a drift-wood bonfire on the beach directly facing the *Curlew*. Fortunately I'd brought a box of matches with me, which I gave to Tajalli, and he soon had the fire roaring. The men standing around it chattered and laughed at the novelty of being away from the camp at such a time and with the "white Missus" sharing the fire.

Tajalli told me to keep one lamp and give the other to a somewhat unsure Tajurra. I saw that the bow anchor had been put into the dinghy which was standing some distance away from the line of action that Tajalli now took to get the boat afloat: he sent me ahead with the lamp to the boat's stern on the starboard side, and then he ranged the men along the boat's side, now knee-deep in the rising tide, and ordered them to take hold of the gunwale.

With me at the stern with my lamp, Tajurra standing amidship with his, and the glaring flames of the fire to discourage any debbil-debbils that may have been around, the Oonas began the lifting and easing of the *Curlew* up, little by little, until the tide righted her on an even keel to float at last!

But the job was not over yet, and the men gladly ran from the water to get back to the comforting fire alongside Mum.

By that time the dinghy was afloat, so Tajalli got into the bow, Tajurra with his lamp in the stern, and I took up the oars and rowed out to the deep water with Tajalli holding on to the anchor rope to haul the *Curlew*'s bow around to face north ready for our leaving the next morning.

Tajalli dropped the bow anchor to moor the boat, and then we rowed around to the stern and he lifted out the anchor from the well-deck and called out to me, "All right, Jimmy, you pull boat back now—quick!"

I rowed the dinghy stern first until the anchor rope tautened and stopped the dinghy. He dropped the anchor overboard ... The job was done.

Back at the beach we moored the dinghy and when we stepped out the tide was lapping into the fire. Mum said to me, "Jimmy, I think you and Tajurra had better light Tajalli and the men back to the camp."

"All right, Mum," I answered and followed her up the bank with Tajalli and the others. Tajurra brought up the rear with his lamp.

The darkness and the procession in the lamplight were more than enough to silence the Oonas in their haste to get home. We showed Mum to the front steps, where Tajalli gave her the box of matches and thanked her. Then we resumed our silent single file, hurrying over to the camp. Once we reached the outskirts our leave-taking was brief, Tajurra handing me his lamp and all of them running like ebony demons for the camp fires.

Why I did it, I don't know, but something drew me to the mia-mia at the bend of the creek. There at one side of the opening to the mia-mia, perched on a stick driven into the ground, was the skull of a baby dolphin . . .

A weird sensation of the unknown swept over me—the same sensation that I had felt under the pandanus palms when I stood there and saw that bone hanging motionless above me . . . Then it was my turn to run for the security of my mother and the house.

8

It was not until I was standing on the beach with Mum the next morning that I realized she was going to be left all alone just because I wanted to find out what had happened at that secret hideout beyond the Gumrai-Gumrai swamp. Perhaps if I had known what lay ahead I might have had second thoughts about getting involved in the weird corroboree rituals that had been planned by the Burunji and Oona elders at their meeting under the pandanus palms.

Mum was holding a parcel of trade tobacco and matches for Tajalli to take with him as a goodwill present. I said to her, "Mum, will you be all right while I'm away?"

"Well, now," she answered brightly, obviously intent on keeping sentiment out of our goodbyes. "Don't you think we should leave unsaid any doubts we may have, Jimmy. I'm your mother and I suppose I've just got to get used to the fact that you're growing up and have to do the things you believe you should do. In any case, Tajalli will see you come to no harm."

"Thanks, Mum," was all I could say to that. "Anyway, here's Tajalli and Tajurra now."

Tajalli in his khaki rig-out and Tajurra, like me, dressed in navy-blue shorts and shirt were hurrying along the beach, leaving the entire Oona tribe standing in front of the camp. Each was carrying a bundle of rolled up blankets.

They came up to us saying, "G'day, Missus. G'day, Jimmy." Mum handed Tajalli the gift of tobacco and matches and said, "Just something to keep that old pipe of yours going, Tajalli. And don't forget to look after yourself."

"Thanks, Missus. Me will." He took the parcel and walked down to the dinghy moored at the water's edge, turned and waved to us in time to see Mum turn from hugging me goodbye to do the same to Tajurra. We hurried down to the dinghy and Tajalli rowed us out, tied up the dinghy astern and stepped aboard. He clambered along the gunwale to the bow to wait for us to get aboard. While I went into the cabin and climbed up into the driving-seat, Tajurra began hauling in the stern anchor. I signalled to Tajalli to lift the bow anchor, as I started the motor. With both anchors aboard, I let in the clutch at slow speed, waved to Mum, and then concentrated on steering the boat with Tajalli standing in the bow to direct me, to make sure that I kept to the deep water.

A shout of farewell and a wild waving of arms came from the Oonas as we swung to starboard into the channel and out to the open sea between the Great Barrier Reef and the mainland. Once clear of the channel, we turned north for the run. In strict accordance with Mum's instructions to me not to let the engine have full throttle at any time, I pulled the quadrant lever down to three-quarter speed and settled down to enjoy the smooth sensation of the *Curlew* cutting her way through the clear blue-green water at a steady six knots.

There was really no need to worry about hitting any of the lesser reefs that dot the coastline if the boat was kept to the main shipping channel that extends all the way between the coast and the Great Barrier Reef up to and beyond the tip of Cape York. It was simply a matter of obeying Tajalli's occasional signals to keep to the deep water. No amount of coaxing could get him away from his seat on the hatch-cover while the boat was under way. In any case, he was enjoying himself with his pipe and the unaccustomed pleasure of not having anything else to do.

Tajurra came and stood alongside me at the wheel to ask, "How about me steer 'im by and by, Jimmy?"

"OK," I agreed. "Smoke-o time, me make tea, you steer."

He grinned and a sudden thought struck me. "That little fella head belonga Burunji fish, longa that mia-mia, Tajurra. What for Tajalli and Trokka put 'im there?"

The grin left his face as quickly as it had appeared. He said, "No more like talk about that thing, Jimmy. By and by that thing make man come longa Oonaderra. By and by that man die."

"What man?" I asked impatiently.

He looked through the cabin glass at Tajalli sitting on the hatch before he would reply. "No more talk about it. By and by Burunjis make corroboree; you see what them Burunji men do; when you see corroboree, you see what happen long time ago when white men go longa bad place longa Gumrai-Gumrai swamp, longa hole in high rock. Debbil-debbils stay longa that hole now, Jimmy. Burunji men no more go longa that hole now; too scared."

"Where they make corroboree?" I asked. "Longa Burunji camp?"

"No," he answered promptly. "We all go longa that bad fella place, longa high rock, make corroboree there. Now that talk stick go back longa old men; by and by Burunji men tell debbil-debbils go away. Tajalli want you go longa that hole longa high rock longa 'im when Burunjis make corroboree."

"Me!" I exclaimed in astonishment. "Me go longa Tajalli! What for?"

The grin crept back on to his face as he answered, "Burunji men say you got red hair all the same god he think live longa Dreamtime; come down longa ground one day, help black men do good fella things, stop all the trouble other white men do."

Although he was grinning he was not joking about the Aborigines' belief that a red-haired god would one day come from the Dreamtime down to earth to help the Aborigines do whatever they wanted.

The fact that Tajurra knew the tribal secrets of his people was quite in accordance with their custom of relating those secrets to all those men who have passed the initiation ritual of body cicatricing and the ordeal by fire, as practised by the Oona tribe, that makes them worthy men of their tribe. Tajurra had passed that test, with honour.

The fact that I was accepted as his blood-brother was quite all right by me; but to be singled out for something I knew little about, just because I happened to have red hair, was something that I had not even contemplated as a reason for travelling to Burunji territory.

Anyway, it was no use badgering Tajurra for more than he wanted to reveal, so I let it go for the time being.

It says a lot for Tajurra's capacity to learn quickly anything he was shown, that he remembered all my previous instructions on the handling of the *Curlew*. At smoke-o and again at lunchtime when I let him take her over while I boiled the billy on the galley kerosene stove and made tea and corned beef sandwiches with pickles, he handled the boat every bit as well as I could. Of course Tajalli, who was given his eats and a mug of tea through the cabin window, made sure to tell him to "Look out all the time longa me, me tell you what to do, Tajurra," and went back to his seat on the hatch-cover to have his eats there, with Tajurra's assurance that he would do exactly as his dad told him.

And so the trip progressed smoothly and pleasantly, with plenty to see. Flying fish skimmed the surface on either side of us as barracouta and other predators harried them in pursuit of a meal. There were also the familiar dorsal fins of sharks cruising on the surface in search of prey. Flotillas of pelicans appeared every mile or so, too, tranquilly feeding, while overhead the gulls, black-capped noddies and various other sea birds blended into the blue-white canopy of the heavens all around and above us.

At about two-thirty, Tajurra left the wheel to me while he tried his luck at trolling for fish with line and hook baited with a piece of white canvas made into a tube which he slipped over the hook to hide it. With the line tied to a stern post of the well-deck canopy he threw out about sixty foot of the line to allow the tube to spin in the water to attract whatever fish might be lured to attack it.

Long after he and I had forgotten the line was out, he was chatting to me when suddenly the boat jerked as though we had hit something. Tajurra dashed for the line as Tajalli came running to the open cabin window. "What you hit? What you do?" he demanded and then caught sight of Tajurra trying to haul in the heavy cord line.

In a flash Tajalli was over the well-deck canopy and out on the stern overhang-platform, heaving and pulling on the line with Tajurra.

I slowed the boat down to idling speed to let them get the fish aboard. It took the best part of a half-hour to drag the huge fish on to the stern platform; it was a big threshing, snapping kingfish—over four feet long and all of thirty-five pounds in weight.

I could only sit and glance back occasionally as the struggle went on to subdue the huge fish. Tajalli finally killed it with a blow from the tomahawk Tajurra got from the locker under the well-deck seats.

"That good fella tucker," he said to Tajurra. "Now you clean 'im." He then ran back over the canopy to his station and waved to me to get under way again.

I pressed the quadrant lever back to three-quarter speed and we resumed our steady six knots an hour while poor old Tajurra had the job of cleaning out the catch on the stern platform with the raucous sea birds diving on to the innards he tossed overboard into our foaming wake. It was more than likely that there were sharks following us out there by that time; and the thought that my friend could slip off that platform prompted me to call out to him, "Hey! Tajurra, more better you come inside."

He laughed and clambered over into the well-deck, dragging the cleaned fish with him. From there he finished the job by cutting three steaks from behind the severed head; each steak, one for each of us, was large enough almost to cover the big frying pan in the galley.

Then I saw Tajalli standing up and gazing ahead at something far away in the distance. He came to the cabin window and bent down to tell me, "Island up there, Jimmy. You stop boat longa it, by and by when I tell you."

"OK," I answered as he ran back to his lookout.

With that extraordinary vision of the Aborigines he had spotted the tiny island while it was still at least three miles away on our starboard side.

Half an hour later, with Tajurra standing beside me watching through the cabin window, Tajalli motioned with his hand and I slowed down. When Tajalli picked up the bow anchor, I switched off the motor, and he dropped the anchor overboard. After a very pleasant eight and a half hours of sailing we had reached a tiny uninhabited island—we were in the lee of the self-same island where the boat of the murderous white men had anchored.

As soon as Tajalli had satisfied himself that the boat was safely anchored, he came and joined Tajurra and me out in the well-deck. He said, looking at the cleaned fish, "More better take that fish longa Burunji now. You two fella stop here, cook fish. Me come back soon."

Without further ado, he hauled the dinghy to the stern platform and Tajurra and I handed the fish down to him. We watched him row across to the Burunjis waiting on the beach to welcome him.

95

Suddenly the water around us became alive with dolphins leaping and frolicking and "talking" that peculiar language they use when they are at play. We watched them, fascinated by their behaviour, until Tajurra said, "More better we get this fella fish cooked; Tajalli say he come back soon."

"OK."

By the time Tajalli returned and clambered into the well-deck we had the fish steaks cooked and a pan full of potato-chips sizzling on the galley stove alongside the simmering billy to make tea.

He sniffed the aroma of our culinary efforts and remarked happily, "Mmm, real good fella tucker, eh?"

And so it turned out, with slabs of bread Mum had sent on to the boat with the other stores for our comfort and convenience. But I'm afraid she would not have approved of our eating cross-legged on the well-deck floor with our plates on our knees, using our fingers instead of knives and forks. Saves a lot of washing up.

While we ate, I asked Tajalli about the dolphins playing around the boat. He laughed and said, "Dolphins live longa this island all the time. Burunji people like dolphins, no more hurt 'im. Suppose Burunji people swim longa this place, not get scared longa sharks; sharks scared longa dolphins."

"What for sharks get scared?"

"Dolphin chase shark, hit 'im all the time longa belly; shark no more like that, clear out altogether."

And so I learned one more lesson in the ways of creatures in the wild; creatures that seem almost to be able to reason and speak and act in the interests of humans as well as themselves. It seemed to me that those dolphins meant a lot to the Burunji tribe for the very good reason that their great totemic god is also a dolphin.

After we had tidied up the galley and washed up I switched on the radio in the cabin to get the evening news, which was routinely ordinary followed by a non-committal weather report that "Cape York will be experiencing the usual dry season of fine weather for the next day or so." So I rejoined Tajalli and Tajurra in the well-deck and we spent the next hour or so listening to Cairns Radio, dinner music interspersed with the usual ads. I lit a hurricane lamp and hung it from the hook on the canopy's ceiling.

Both Tajurra and Tajalli enjoyed the novelty of relaxing away from their usual nights around the tribal camp fires. Then it was bedtime, but when I suggested they sleep in the cabin, both laughed, shook their heads and Tajalli said, "No more like sleep in there, Jimmy; more better we sleep here." He tapped his foot on the floor. And that was that.

Tajurra got his bundle—two blankets—spread one out on the floor, kicked off his boots, lay down and pulled the other blanket up to his chin, while Tajalli clambered along the gunwale and brought his bundle from where he had kept it by the hatch-cover.

Chatting, laughing and jokingly remarking that, "Oona men no more soft fellas, sleep longa beds," Tajalli laid one folded blanket alongside Tajurra's, then lay down between its folds after carefully arranging the other blanket as his pillow in which I guessed he had rolled up his lap-lap and tribal headband.

We said Goodnight and I went and turned off the radio. In place of a camp fire I left the lamp burning low, for Tajalli's and Tajurra's peace of mind. Then I hopped into a lower bunk and was asleep in moments ...

By sun-up the next morning we had breakfasted on pufftaloons and bacon and had the dinghy provisioned with tinned foods, potatoes and onions, a twenty-pound tin of prepared flour which Mum had pre-mixed to make it easier for us to bake a damper, or johnny cakes, when we wished to do so. Tajalli checked with me to see that plates, mugs,

97

spoons, a carving knife and a tin opener were among the billy-cans we were taking along for cooking and making tea, as well as an enamel dish and the hurricane lamp. We took our blanket rolls, of course; even the citronella.

The amount of stuff we had made me ask Tajalli if it would be too much for us to carry across the Gumrai-Gumrai swamp. He laughed and said, "We no more carry this stuff, Jimmy—we go longa swamp, take dinghy."

That surprised me because I had not imagined we could do such a thing. But he was right.

Remembering Mum's instructions to check everything before leaving the *Curlew* at any time, I made a round of the boat to see that all cabin windows and the rear cabin door were shut against the possibility of rain coming in. One last check: I lifted the floor flap in the well-deck . . . All was in order, there was no water in the bilge.

Tajurra rowed us ashore at the mouth of the creek that flowed past the north side of the Burunji camp. We stepped ashore and moored the dinghy to the shouting, laughter and greetings of all the Burunjis waiting for us.

But our welcome was brief. Kammaluk and five other men, two of whom I had met under the pandanus palms on Oonaderra, were ready for the journey, wearing lap-laps and each carrying a killing spear and a three-pronged fishing spear.

After a brief exchange between Kammaluk and Tajalli, the Burunji leader looked at me, hatless, and said, "White fella Jimmy!" in evident satisfaction that I had turned up to keep the appointment to attend the secret corroboree. Then he touched my hair respectfully before turning to Tajalli, who nodded and said to me, "All right now, Jimmy; you go longa Tajurra, take dinghy up longa creek. Me go longa Burunji men, walk longa them."

"OK," I answered and noted that Tajalli's shirt-front

bulged with what I rightly guessed was his lap-lap and tribal headband—status symbols of tribal elders and leaders that must be worn on all great occasions.

Tajurra and I got back into the dinghy and I began the first lap of the never-to-be-forgotten journey into the fastnesses of the wilderness of Cape York Peninsula. I was to be present at a Stone Age ceremony of primitive men to lift a taboo that had for more than a quarter of a century delayed the meting out of retribution against a man of their own tribe, who had broken a tribal law by killing a woman—the woman who belonged to their tribal leader. Even under the greatest provocation no Aboriginal man or woman has the authority to kill another—that authority is the sole prerogative of the tribal elders who instruct the leader to carry out their sentence of death.

Half an hour at the oars was enough for me, so Tajurra took over. Some way ahead on the south bank of the creek Tajalli, now wearing his lap-lap and headband, was travelling with the Burunji party—all similarly dressed and all now carrying only the three-pronged spears required by ritual. They kept that distance ahead of us through that open forest dotted everywhere with white ant nests, some taller than a man. These nests—called termitaria—are constructed of soil, grit and saliva by wood-eating ants which also make tunnels over the forest floor through which they go in search of dead and dying trees that make up their food supply.

As we progressed we caught sight of 'roos and wallabies bounding away through the trees. The Burunji men didn't bother to try and spear them because they knew that ahead lay water containing all they would need in the way of food for that day.

Just when I thought I would have to take another stint at the oars, the party ahead stopped and waited for us. By the time we reached them, they had begun to cross the creek which had now shallowed. Tajalli called out to us, "All right, more better you walk now, pull 'im dinghy."

We kicked off our boots and got out. Pulling the dinghy by the bow, Tajurra and I followed the party into a narrow side creek lined on either side by Epacrid forest—a weird conglomeration of low-growing gnarled and twisted trees.

The men continued along the bank of the creek while we trudged on in the shallow water. At the time I was not aware that the job of pulling the dinghy along was really a favour bestowed on us when later, in the swamp, we would be glad of the support of the dinghy's bow. And so we went on through that weird and silent forest, with only the occasional cawing of a crow to remind us that all around us there were living creatures, silent and invisible while we were in the vicinity. Behind us in the distance, the call of cockatoos, parrots and pigeons sounded like echoes in a Dante landscape of wilderness.

In the early afternoon the Epacrid forest abruptly gave way to rain forest; we continued along the creek for about another half mile until, as suddenly as it began, the jungle ended in a bare sandy area with tall swamp grass ahead, through which the creek was flowing.

The Burunjis stopped for us to catch up, then Kammaluk spoke to Tajalli, who nodded and turned to tell me, "We camp here, Jimmy." And he pulled the dinghy up on to the sand and began to unload the gear while the Burunjis, after sticking their spears in the sand, went into the rain forest to break branches off the saplings.

Tajalli told Tajurra and me to get "Plenty good fella wood, make big fire, here." He pointed to the spot for the fire and Tajurra and I began dragging fallen timber out of the rain forest until we had a stack built and more lying beside it.

With the talking and chattering and movement that went on while the camp fire was prepared, I had not noticed, until I paused, the odd soughing sound that came from the swamp grass swaying in the weird wind blowing over the Gumrai-Gumrai that lay beyond that head-high wall of grass. It was an indescribable sound of loneliness, like something out of a phantasmagoria imagined in the dead hours of the night.

I shuddered and looked at Tajalli and Tajurra who were listening, too. A sudden blind fear of being alone in that eerie place took hold of me ... I walked up to Tajalli and so did Tajurra, for the security he could give us in that haunting wilderness of the Never-Never country we had entered.

Tajalli, that man of quiet courage, said, smiling at us, "No more get fright longa that funny fella wind, Jimmy, Tajurra; 'im just cry all the same my people; we cry all the same that wind, Jimmy; cry longa bad things we know about other people."

But our mood of apprehension soon passed when Tajalli put a match to the stacked fire and it roared up into a crackling bonfire ... and not too soon—sandflies and mosquitoes began a voracious biting of the exposed parts of my arms, face, neck and legs ... Only by standing to the windward of the fire's smoke could I repel them; but the moment I moved away from the fire they were at me again. The bottle of citronella ... I dashed for the dinghy, got the bottle and frantically swabbed myself.

Tajalli and Tajurra seemed to be oblivious of mosquitoes, because they were moving freely around the camp, not even swatting themselves.

I put the bottle back into the dinghy as the Burunjis returned, each armed with a dense-leaved branch. Kammaluk motioned for silence as four of the men moved downstream to take up their positions while the other man moved up to where the creek emerged from the swamp grass. Holding his branch in his right hand, he began to throw into the slow-flowing water something he was taking from his mouth. I thought it a strange procedure until I saw the water ahead of him begin to churn and splash as he took more of the things from his mouth to throw them farther downstream . . . Then I saw one of the things land on the water: it was a mullee grub—a large white edible grub that lives in rotting timber on the jungle floor. It no sooner hit the water than it was snapped up by one of the churning fish.

Then the man throwing the grubs began to beat the water with his branch to drive the fish towards the men downstream, who in turn began to swish their branches backwards and forwards in the water as Kammaluk and Tajalli picked up their fishing spears and, one on each side of the stream, began plunging their spears into the water. In this way they caught at least a dozen glistening barramundis and the spearing ended with the men collecting the fish and bringing them to the fireside, breaking their silence in excited chattering and laughter.

Long before sunset we had everything cooking; the barramundis were placed whole in the coals, and Tajurra helped me to get a gallon billy-can of onions and spuds, in their jackets, boiling merrily on the fire with a similar billy-can of water for tea. Tajalli said we were to share everything with the Burunjis, which suited me fine, and we ate the baked fish along with the vegetables, washed down with hot, sweet black tea.

The mosquitoes and sandflies, of course, were still around until another fire was lit so that we could lie between the two in peace. That night we slept under our blankets, and the Burunjis curled up on the bare sand, protected by the heat and smoke of the fires.

The unaccustomed work of that day guaranteed that I fell asleep quickly, and it seemed only moments before I was awake again. Daylight crept over the tree tops to the eerie sound of that mourning wind coming over the Gumrai-Gumrai swamp ahead of us.

The Gumrai-Gumrai—named by the Aborigines "Endless Swamp"—is a desolate wilderness of crying wind moaning across seemingly endless miles of swamp and ooze in which the animal life mainly consists of tortoises and water snakes, inured to the place by virtue of Nature's law of the survival of the fittest.

Being the Dry Season, the depth of water was reduced to about a foot; it was then that I realized why Kammaluk had decided to use the dinghy to carry our things in; to have had to carry loads on our backs would have increased unbearably the agony of what we had to face. The Burunjis were in the lead and Tajalli with them, each carrying only a fishing spear. Tajurra and I were pulling the dinghy along by the bow and finding it hard to keep up with the men.

Our early camp the previous afternoon had puzzled me until Tajalli explained the logic of it. There is no place in the swamp to stop or camp; since it would take even the fastest, fittest of Aborigines at least eight hours or more to cross it, the reason for our delayed start until early the next morning became abundantly clear to me when I looked ahead to the distant ranges where our rendezvous was to be.

As we progressed farther into the swamp under the increasing heat of the ascending sun I realized that the sandflies and mosquitoes had ceased their attacks because the Burunjis were carefully avoiding all of the "islands" where the swamp grass grows on any patch of soil above the water. It is on these "islands" that the winged pests can get into the shade of the grass to settle there; any disturbance of that grass or lingering in its shade would have meant not only being attacked by sandflies and mosquitoes but also by voracious leeches, which could be seen on the swamp grass waving their sucking snouts at the smell of the men passing by; one touch of that grass would have meant a horde of the blood-suckers fastening on to us. That would also mean a loss of blood when they were pulled off our flesh, and in that swamp we needed every ounce of strength just to keep moving. But we had to guard continually against leeches in the water, too, by checking that they were removed from our legs before they could get a hold on us.

Coupled with all the blood-sucking pests was the rising heat and blinding glare from the stinking water being stirred up and ... worse still ... the terrible moaning sound of the hot wind that never stopped its crying all around us.

We had to drink sparingly from the couple of billies of water we had brought from the creek. For lunch we ate the remainder of the barramundi that we had brought along, not stopping but eating our portions and taking a sip of the water as it was passed along to the men by Tajurra from the dinghy. And so that terrible day wore on.

By about three o'clock I had had it. Tajurra called out to Tajalli, "Hey! Jimmy, knock up now; maybe he get sick!"

The men stopped and Tajalli came running back to see what was the matter. "You get sick longa belly, Jimmy?" he asked in consternation at the sight of me sitting on the bow of the boat.

"No more sick longa belly," I answered wearily, "me just get knocked up; too much tired now."

He flicked a marsh fly off my bare arm and said, "Come on, you get in longa dinghy."

Before I could protest, he lifted me into the stern of the boat and dragged my blanket around me with the admonition that I "Stop longa boat. By and by soon we go longa camp longa there." He pointed up ahead to the ramparts of the cliffs where they sweep for miles like a giant barrier encompassing the Gumrai-Gumrai against any penetration of its wilderness by men, except those who, for thousands of years, have had the power to do so—the Aborigines.

"OK, Tajalli," I said. Then he went and took my place alongside Tajurra and we moved on again.

And so I sat huddled and dozing in the confines of my blanket in the stern of the dinghy for the rest of the journey. A sudden scraping of the dinghy jerked me awake. We had reached the edge of the swamp. For about twenty-five yards the ground sloped from the water's edge up to what looked like a gigantic pipe organ of at least a hundred-and-fifty foot high columns of greeny-black basalt . . . and the wind . . . that endless moaning wind.

I looked around and saw behind me in the water the Burunjis standing with Tajalli and Tajurra, all watching me.

I got up and stepped out of the blanket on to the ground. Then Tajalli came up to me and said, "You all right now, Jimmy?"

"Too right," I answered, because I did feel recovered and wanted to retrieve my standing in the eyes of the Aborigines.

He smiled a queer little smile, then said, "You no more get fright longa this place, Jimmy?"

Standing there in the long shadow cast by the towering cliff, I did feel uneasy but said, "No more frightened longa this place, Tajalli."

He smiled again and called to the group still in the water. They came out and stood with us, Tajurra beside me.

I saw the Burunjis looking up at the cliff just as Tajurra nudged me and pointed to a place about halfway up it . . . I looked up and saw, in a cleft between the huge basalt columns, a human skull grinning down at us.

9

Our crossing of the Gumrai-Gumrai was not an occasion for celebration as could be seen when we gathered wood and built two roaring fires, one to cook a meal and the other to repel the mosquitoes and sandflies. The Burunjis and Tajalli sat between the fires talking in whispers and glancing up occasionally and anxiously at the skull in the cleft.

If the Aborigines had crossed the swamp without the encumbrance of me and the dinghy they would have travelled faster to allow themselves time to search for and catch tortoises and file snakes for their evening meal before leaving the swamp. As it was, they had to make do with sharing two billies of canned soup into which Tajurra and I put blobs of dough for dumplings we made in the dish. Fortunately there was enough to go round, and it proved to be quite all right for us to use the swamp water if we avoided the places where it had been stirred up by the men. And the boiling of it for the soup and billy of tea was a means of sterilizing it.

There was very little talk after the meal, even when Tajalli handed round his glowing pipe for the Burunjis to share. I suppose that skull and the crying wind that had now turned cold had their effect of dampening any desire for happy talk.

We all slept in a row between the fires. I was next to Tajurra who was soon sound asleep but I was too tired to settle down. Perhaps it was anxiety which kept me awake listening to the crying of that wind and rising above that wind a sound that can only be described as hellish—the screaming calls of catbirds high up in the rain forest fringing the top of the cliffs. As if that were not enough for my taut, apprehensive imagination, there began the maddening calls of the coffin bird. At first the sound only registers as a backdrop to all the other sounds of the night creatures that inhabit the rain forest, then the "Tap, tap, tap tap tap!" of the call and the answering calls starts a maddening obsession in the listener's mind for the taps to begin all over again.

Long after the camp was asleep I lay listening until the boon of sleep swept me at last into oblivion . . .

I awoke in bright sunlight to find Tajurra tending the fires. I sat up and saw Tajalli and the Burunjis already out in the swamp with their spears.

As soon as I sat up Tajurra came over to me, evidently scared about something, and said, "Jimmy, me get big fella fright—bones belonga dead man longa there." He pointed to the base of the cliff directly below the cleft.

I stood up and looked across but could see nothing, so I made to walk over there and he said, "No, Jimmy, maybe we wait, tell Tajalli, eh?"

But Tajalli was hurrying out of the swamp carrying a file snake on the end of his three-pronged fishing spear. He dumped the snake and spear near the cooking fire and looking intently at me asked, "You all right now, Jimmy?"

"Yes," I answered. "Feel all right now, Tajalli. But Tajurra say bones belonga dead man over there."

He didn't even look in that direction. He just said, "Yes, bones belonga white man, other white man shoot 'im long time ago. By and by we fix them bones."

In the bright sunlight it was easier for me to show my courage, so I said, "Me go look longa that man, Tajalli."

He didn't try to stop me. All he said was, "Jimmy, debbil-debbil stop longa them bones; stop longa 'im, too." He pointed up at the white grinning skull looking down on us from the cleft and added, "That white man, too. You go there." He pointed again, this time at the base of the cliff, and cautioned me not to touch the bones.

I walked over with his and Tajurra's eyes following my every movement. There in a narrow runnel, worn out of the rock foot of the cliff's base by centuries of rain coursing down the cliff, lay a skeleton with a bullet hole in the skull; both of its thighs were smashed, showing that the body had probably fallen feet first down the cliff. Then I looked up at the other skull and could plainly see a bullet hole in its forehead. I turned and hurried back to the fires.

When I looked at Tajalli for the answer to this mystery, he just shrugged and said, "Wait, Jimmy; by and by we go longa there, get shield, get little fella bag belonga Kammaluk; bring shield bring bag, give it Kammaluk; by and by we make corroboree, you see what other white man do."

And there the matter stood until after we had had a mug of tea with the Burunjis who had brought back tortoises for baking later.

The main purpose was first to get Tajalli and me into that cleft to retrieve a shield and a woven human-hair bag of sacred objects belonging to Kammaluk. I was not allowed to learn why they had been left there over a quarter of a century before, because tribal law prohibits the lifting of a tribal taboo or curse until a ceremonial corroboree has been held by the elders to placate the debbil-debbil guardians of that curse or taboo. Later I was to hear the story and also to learn that my red hair was a protection against the debbil-debbils so that Tajalli and I could enter the cursed area with immunity.

As soon as the sweet black tea had been drunk, Tajalli went to the dinghy and undid the anchor rope, which was made of strong manilla cordage. Then he spoke to Kammaluk who was sitting at the water's edge, flanked by the other Burunjis, all silently looking up at the cleft in the rock face.

After a brief discussion between the two leaders, Kammaluk looked over his shoulder across the swamp towards the

rising sun before turning again to Tajalli to nod his
agreement.

Tajalli then tied one end of the anchor rope around his
waist and came back carrying the coiled rope around his neck
to where I was standing between the fires with Tajurra. He
said, "Jimmy, Kammaluk want you come longa there longa
me. All right?"

"What for?" I asked, looking fearfully at the forbidding
cliff.

"No tell you now, Jimmy," he answered. "By and by, all
right?"

Before answering I looked at Kammaluk and the other
Burunjis, all staring intently at me, waiting for my reaction to
Tajalli's request to accompany him into that cleft leading to
the sacred initiation caves of the Burunjis. Then Kammaluk
said eagerly, "White fella Jimmy, *sibba? Sibba?*" I nodded
and answered, "*Sibba*," and the immediate "Wah!" of
congratulation from the squatting Burunjis made me realize
that the die was cast. I could not back out now. If I did, I
would forever lose the trust of the Aborigines who believed
that my red hair was a badge of godliness, that I had been sent
by their god, the great dolphin in the sky, to help in the lifting
of the curse from their sacred caves and the objects that lay in
there waiting to be returned to Kammaluk, the man who had
invoked that curse to prevent the objects from falling into the
hands of white men.

Tajalli then asked me to bring matches and the hurricane
lamp from the dinghy and follow him. I put the box of
matches in my pocket and held the lamp while he tied the
other end of the rope securely round my waist. Then I gave
him the lamp and he said, "Take 'im boot off, Jimmy."

I kicked off my boots, knowing that Tajalli had asked this
for the simple reason that the boots of white men leave tracks.

Without another word he took the handle of the lamp in his

teeth and literally sprang up the cliff to gain a foothold and handhold in the tiny crevices he had picked out before he leapt. Then, like a spider monkey, he began the climb, not once looking back until he reached the cleft and carefully pulled himself past that grinning skull. Next he put down the lamp, turned round and called out, "All right, Jimmy," as he began hauling up the rope until it was taut. Again he called out, "Right, Jimmy, now! Jump!" and heaved on the rope as I leapt upwards to grab at the rock face. But I had no need to grab at anything because he was hauling me up in powerful jerks, hand over hand, never pausing until he had hauled me clean through the cleft, which was actually as high and as wide as a house door, and not the narrow cleft it appeared to be from below.

He drew me at once away from the skeleton which lay as the man had fallen, face down, his head peering over the floor of the cleft. But Tajalli was intent on getting rid of the rope, so we undid it and coiled and laid it by the wall of what was really a long, dark, narrow tunnel.

Then he picked up the lamp, but didn't light it—he just stood waiting and looking out through the cleft at Tajurra and the Burunjis away down below, silently watching us. Then Tajalli touched me on the shoulder and said, "See, sun come in now, Jimmy," and pointed at the sloping floor of the tunnel. And indeed the rays of the rising sun had reached the cleft and were beginning to lengthen into the tunnel, until within a minute or so the tunnel was lit all the way down as far as we could see.

"Come on, quick!" he said, and led the way down . . . down . . . down along the eerie tunnel that Nature had blown out millions of years ago in the explosion that had sent the lava torrents cascading into the sea that once covered this part of Cape York Peninsula and thus created the gigantic pipe organ cliffs we were entering—the first men to do so in more than a quarter of a century.

Then abruptly we had to stop, because the tunnel ended in a barrier of rock. At its foot was a narrow opening—a horizontal slit in the rock about three feet wide and approximately eighteen inches high. From the other side there came the sound of running water.

Tajalli whispered, "Matches, Jimmy."

I gave him the box and he opened the lamp, lit and closed it, and put the matchbox back into my shirt pocket. Then he squeezed through the opening, holding the lamp ahead of him. Once through, he called back to me, "Come on."

In I went, and with his help crawled through to stand beside him on the rock floor, some four feet lower than the tunnel. Holding the lamp above his head he looked around. We were in a very large, circular cave. The water I had heard was an underground stream that flowed from the base of the cave wall on our right through the centre of the chamber to disappear under the rock wall on our left in a gurgling, swirling torrent that sounded as though it were being sucked down by a giant with a huge drinking straw.

Tajalli tapped me on the shoulder and pointed upwards. To my intense surprise, instead of the roof I expected to see, there was nothing . . . until my eyes focused on a seemingly small hole far, far above, encircling a dark sky dotted with—stars! I was seeing what miners or deep well-sinkers often see in broad daylight from the bottom of a deep shaft—a starry sky.

Tajalli, still looking up, whispered, "By and by sun come up longa there, look down longa this place. Come on." He hurried across the cave floor and I followed close behind to keep within the lamplight. We waded over the stream, which was not deep, and entered what was really an ante-chamber. In the middle of the floor, by the ashes of an ancient fire, there was a big, gold-lipped pearl shell with a knife fashioned from a similar shell inside it. The dark-brown stain in the shell and on the knife spoke clearly of the blood ritual that had been carried out long ago in the ceremony of initiating the Burunji boys into manhood, when it was interrupted by the events that were soon to be re-enacted, in the corroboree to cleanse the place of its taboo.

But it was not these things that Tajalli wanted. With the light held above his head, he walked to a ledge on the chamber wall. He handed me the lamp and then reached up to lift down Kammaluk's shield with the dolphin etched into it in white gypsum flanked by the two Z marks of tribal identification of the Burunji tribe.

He put the shield on the floor, totem face up. Then he reached up again to run his hand along the ledge until, with an exclamatory "Wah", he brought down the woven human-hair bag that I knew must belong to Kammaluk.

I thought I was going to get a glimpse of the bag's sacred contents but I was wrong. When I said, "Come on, Tajalli, open it!" he looked at me and said, "No. This fella bag no belonga me, no belonga you. By and by Kammaluk open 'im. We wait."

In my disappointment I said, "What for Kammaluk not come longa here, get 'im bag?"

"Debbil-debbil, Jimmy, make Kammaluk die, suppose 'im come longa here; make all Burunji people die, suppose anybody come longa here."

"What for you no more die; me no more die?" I insisted foolishly, because I should have known better than to ask such a question.

His quiet answer was, of course, what I should have expected. An Aboriginal curse or taboo—*unless otherwise stated by the elders*—is directed only at members of their own tribe to preserve tribal laws and punishments strictly to themselves. His answer was simple, "Debbil-debbils no more hurt you, no more hurt me—you all the same god; got 'im red hair."

"Kammaluk make other white men die, eh?" I asked, remembering the two skeletons with bullet holes in their skulls.

He shrugged and said, "Yes, maybe." And that was all he would volunteer to satisfy my curiosity about the two men. "More better we go now," he said, picking up the shield in one hand and carrying the bag in the other. I followed him with the lamp across the stream back to the opening in the barrier of rock. He slipped the shield and bag through into the tunnel. Then, turning to me, he said, "Look!" and pointed upwards.

I looked . . . The sun was shining now and we could see the canopy of the rain forest fringing the opening far above. The smooth, perpendicular walls of rock were festooned with a variety of staghorn and elkhorn ferns, crowsnest ferns, long trailing tassel and cedar ferns, with orchids and maiden hair ferns growing wherever they could get a foothold in the damp rock face. It was a fantastic sight of rain forest plants in a setting far different from their usual habitat in the jungles of Cape York.

But the most pressing need of the moment was to follow Tajalli safely with the lamp; how we needed that lamp! The sun, having risen above the cliffs outside, had left the tunnel again in almost total darkness except for the pin-point of light in the cleft we hurried to.

The excitement that broke out on the ground when Tajalli appeared in the cleft holding up the bag and shield was wild enough for the sound to come echoing up to us from the Burunjis below.

Warily avoiding the skeleton lying along the tunnel wall, Tajalli tied the rope around me and said, "All right, Jimmy, go out now."

While he held the rope taut I knelt down and eased myself backwards out of the cleft. Holding the lamp in my left hand, and clutching the rope with the other, I began the descent by kicking myself clear of the cliff face as he lowered me hand over hand almost to within reach of the ground, when he stopped to call down to me, "Kick hard, Jimmy!"

I did, just as he slackened the rope to let me land on the ground away from the other skeleton lying in the runnel.

A "Wah!" of approval came from the Burunjis still squatting along the water's edge with Tajurra beside them. It seemed odd to me that no one came to help, especially when Tajalli called down to me, "Take 'im rope off, Jimmy; me send down other things."

I set the lamp on the ground, slipped off the rope and waited while Tajalli hauled it up to lower the shield and bag. He called out again, "Grab 'im, Jimmy!" and swung the rope so that I could grab the shield and pull it clear of the runnel . . . Tajalli then eased off on the rope to let me lower the shield gently to the ground with the bag's draw-string tied to the braided cord of the shield's arm loop.

Tajalli called out to me to undo the rope and he hauled it back, coiling it around his arm until he got it up and dropped it behind him in the tunnel. Then, with the same spider monkey tackle he had used in going up, he began the descent with instinctive, rapid drops to footholds and handholds.

When he leapt back to stand beside me, he put his hand on my shoulder and said quietly, "Jimmy, me happy for you; you good fella; no more scared longa debbil-debbils; you all the same man now. Come, we take things longa Kammaluk; me talk longa 'im, tell you what he say longa me . . . Jimmy!"

A peculiar feeling swept over me. I didn't answer because, standing there in that endless Gumrai-Gumrai wind, I suddenly heard a "whispering" above the crying sound the wind makes day and night. I don't know what words were in that "whispering"; I can only say that the mournful cadence of the wind had taken on an eerie overtone of something presaging ... it was beyond my power to reason what. Perhaps that eeriness was focused through the minds and eyes of the Aborigines; even Tajalli, beside me, was staring at me intently. I stood transfixed, my red hair blowing back from my freckled, ordinary face.

Suddenly his repeated "Jimmy!" broke my hypnotic trance and made me exclaim, "Eh, oh, OK, Tajalli."

He picked up the shield and the bag tied on it and I followed him to put the lamp and my boots in the dinghy while he moved to where Tajurra and the Burunjis were still sitting along the water's edge.

The next thing I knew was that Tajurra was standing beside me saying, "Gee! Jimmy! You do big fella thing go longa that place, get things belonga Kammaluk. Me hear Burunjis talk scared longa you go longa debbil-debbils longa that hole. Burunjis no more scared now; 'im say 'im like you be son longa Kammaluk."

I grinned and was about to tell him that he, being my blood brother, would become Kammaluk's son too, when Tajalli shouted, "Jimmy, come here."

Kammaluk, who had risen and was now holding the shield by the cord in his left hand, was speaking in great excitement to Tajalli. It was translated for me, "Kammaluk very happy now, Jimmy. He ask me ..."

And so for the next ten minutes I was also happy but embarrassed by the praise I as a white boy received for my "bravery" in making the crossing of the Gumrai-Gumrai without complaint, as all Aborigines should. Unlike an Aborigine, I had become, in the eyes of Kammaluk and his elders, a god second in importance to the Burunji god itself. Finally, as Tajurra explained to me, the Burunjis, during our absence in the secret initiation caves, had decided to offer me lifelong membership of their tribe as a reward for helping them to retrieve their sacred objects so that the curse of their god, the great dolphin in the sky, could be removed and the debbil-debbils sent back to the Dreamtime at a corroboree to be held at sundown. Then they would re-enact what the white men had done to invoke the curse which had also fallen on tribespeople who had allowed the murderer to live when tribal law said he should have been put to death.

"You want be brother belonga Burunji people, Jimmy?" Tajalli asked me.

I nodded, and turning to Kammaluk I said, "*Sibba.*"

By that one word I knew I was committed to obey the tribal law of never communicating to white people the secrets of the tribe while its elders and leader who revealed them to me were still alive.

We had had no food, apart from a mouthful of black tea, since the previous night, but Tajalli and Tajurra explained that the Burunjis had been fasting as part of their tribal "penance" for their past mistakes that had brought such calamity on the Burunji people. As Tajalli further explained, now that Tajurra and I were brothers of the Burunjis, we were expected to share all things, good and bad, with them.

Addressing us both he said, "By and by Burunjis eat longa dark; we wait, eh, longa dark, eat longa Burunjis?"

"OK," we both agreed, not altogether willingly because we were starving and we could have eaten anything.

However, the work of preparing for the corroboree now began. Kammaluk and two of the men went out into the swamp while the rest of us gathered firewood where it had fallen from the rain forest above the cliffs. We eventually had a huge pile of hefty branches and logs. Then back from the swamp came the men, two of them carrying a pair of struggling tortoises and Kammaluk with a big bundle of swamp grass. At the water's edge the men spoke to Kammaluk who nodded permission for them to kill the tortoises. They did this by biting them behind the head, in the traditional manner of the Aborigines, and then laid them alongside the six tortoises that had been caught earlier with the big file snake.

Tajalli, Tajurra and I sat beside the dinghy with the men who had been gathering wood. Then came the next step in the preparations for the corroboree. With the two men who had accompanied him into the swamp, Kammaluk squatted at the water's edge and began the weaving of the bundle of swamp grass, in silence, until they had made two large mats, which they then rolled and tied at one end to make a pair of tubes. The left-over grass was plaited into a rope handle, which they fixed to one of the tubes. They then put the two tubes alongside Kammaluk's shield and bag on the ground between the two fires.

After this the men retreated to the water's edge while Kammaluk went back into the swamp alone to fetch another bundle of swamp grass, this time dead, dry grass. Fashioning the stems of the grass into long, plaited lengths, he then fastened them at regular intervals with more of the grass stems to hold them firm and stiff. He made about half a dozen of the things and stacked them on top of the shield, chanting as he did so something I could not hear above the mourning sound of the wind . . .

Although we were forbidden to eat food, there was nothing to prevent us preparing it in readiness for the feast that would follow the corroboree ceremony that night. So, in the late afternoon, as the shadow of the cliff began to lengthen, Tajurra, Tajalli and I prepared the last of our spuds and onions, a gallon billy-full, to go with one of the last two tins of corned beef we had left. The remainder of our supply of flour was kept in reserve for later use. The billies, tortoises and the file snake were then removed to the far side of the cooking fire on the right, away from where the corroboree ritual was to be held. The fire on the left was to be used for another, far more serious purpose.

About an hour before sunset the Burunjis prepared themselves. Working in pairs, each man in turn took a handful of soft white ash from the left side of the non-cooking fire and squatted by the water's edge with the man he was to "decorate" with the symbolic markings worn at their secret ceremonies.

Holding the white ash in his left palm, the first man in each of the three pairs spat saliva into the ash and mixed it into a white paint with his right index finger. Then began the painting of his partner, which took several handfuls of the ash and saliva to complete. When the men stood up in the gathering darkness, I saw that their markings were the same as those the Oonas wear in their secret ceremonies: three horizontal stripes across the forehead, nose and chin, six more across the front of the body from shoulders to lap-lap, and two vertical stripes down both arms and the front of both legs.

The sight of the Burunjis wearing their ceremonial corroboree paint was an eerie sight, made more so by the mourning of the wind. I shuddered in my place with Tajalli and Tajurra by the cooking fire. They remained impassive and silent until Kammaluk stepped away from his tribal elders to come and speak to Tajalli, who nodded his agreement and said to Tajurra and me, "Come away, sit longa dinghy."

The three of us went and sat in the bottom of the dinghy out of the way of the Burunjis, who immediately joined Kammaluk and began piling wood on both fires from the stack we had gathered until the fires were roaring in leaping, dancing flames that cast weird silhouettes on the wall of the cliffs. The men moved behind the fires to begin a rhythmic chanting and dancing, and as the chanting grew louder, so did the echoes from the cliffs, throwing back their shouts of "Burunji! Burunji! Myee Burunji! Myee Wundul!"

On and on it went until that feeling of dread I had previously experienced under the bone in the pandanus palms again took hold of me . . . Then I recognized the words "Myee Wundul!" for what they meant: the Burunjis were not only calling to their god Burunji, but also to the spirit of a murdered woman exactly as I had once heard the Oonas call to a spirit woman on the night of one of their secret corroborees on Oonaderra.

I don't know whether it was the effects of my long fast that made me feel or imagine an odd shifting of the wind, but it seemed to change to a weird sobbing or soughing sound like the wailing of Aboriginal women in lament for their dead.

For about a quarter of an hour the weird chanting and dancing round the fires went on and on, and the accompanying echoes reverberated in the distance along the cliffs.

Then suddenly the ritual stopped, and the men stood between the fires facing the cliffs with their leaping shadows. In the sudden silence the sound of the coffin bird calls came down on the wind, and away up in the rain forest the mournful howl of a scrub dingo answering its mate. I looked up at the starry sky and there, silently gliding over us, were those weird creatures of the night . . . flying foxes.

Tajalli, sitting between Tajurra and me, nudged us and whispered, "Burunji men soon show what 'im think white men do."

It is well known that Aborigines can read the signs of tracks left on the ground by the tiniest of creatures, and now I learned that the Burunjis had pieced together the story not only from what they had seen but from the tracks left all round the camp site by the white men and others. Tajalli suddenly cautioned us to keep silent, and we watched the re-enactment of what had taken place more than a quarter of a century before when the Burunji initiation party, led by Kammaluk, had scaled the cliff and entered the cleft, leaving the two women to attend the cooking fire while the men carried out the initiation of the Burunji boys into manhood. . .

It began with two of the Burunjis taking up their positions at the cooking fire, chattering and laughing in the manner of Aboriginal women. Kammaluk stepped away to stand beside the wood stack a short distance from the other fire, with his back to the scene.

The other three Burunjis played the parts of the three white men . . . suddenly they rushed forward and knocked the two women to the ground. Then, in perfect mimicry, they grabbed the imaginary bundle of rifles by the fire. Seizing the rifles, the men aimed them at the prostrate women. I could see how those three white men, long ago, had waited their chance to leap from the swamp and seize the unsuspecting Aboriginal women whose fire had guided the white men to them.

The next scene followed swiftly. One of the women picked up an imaginary spear. Before the woman could hurl the spear one of the men fired and "bang!", the reverberation of the shout he gave echoed along the cliffs and the woman rolled over and remained still.

Now the man (I later learned that he was the leader) mimed the action of ejecting the spent cartridge from the rifle and reloading with another bullet that he took from the pocket of an imaginary jacket. Then he casually kicked the dead woman over on to her back before giving an order to the other two men, who went through the motions of throwing all the spears into the fire. The other woman (this was Turrapini) lay watching them, terrified.

The leader then kicked her to her feet and spoke to her. She paused for a moment and then nodded and pointed up at the cleft.

At that point in the corroboree the action ceased briefly. The three actors portraying the white men stood looking up at the cliff. Then their leader said something to the woman who answered by pointing to herself and then to the cleft. He then prodded her with his rifle and gave her an order. She called out, "Kammaluk! Kammaluk! Kammaluk!" in a voice loud enough to carry to the secret initiation cave.

The re-enactment proceeded and I knew that this was what had actually happened as Kammaluk, standing by the wood stack, prepared to throw his voice to repeat what he had said twenty-five years ago when the real Turrapini calling his name had brought him from the secret cave. Kammaluk shouted up at the cleft and his voice echoed back as though it was coming from inside: "Turrapini! Turrapini!" followed by a stream of Aboriginal words.

Suddenly the man playing the white leader raised his imaginary rifle and aimed it at the cleft just as Turrapini yelled out a warning. As the man then appeared to press the trigger, Turrapini knocked his arm, throwing him off balance. He turned on her and gave her a vicious kick which sent her to the ground.

The scene continued with Turrapini being made to lie face down beside the dead woman and the men waiting, watching the cleft.

In the ensuing silence, Tajalli whispered, "Turrapini sister belonga me, woman belonga Kammaluk; white man keep Turrapini alive."

"What for?" I whispered back.

"Turrapini speak pidgin all the same me; white man tell her what to do when he find out she talk little bit white fella talk."

121

And so I found out that the white man had kept Turrapini alive to help him get out of the swamp.

But the next scene showed that vicious man eliminating his two friends by first sending one of them to scale the cliff. This was shown by one of the other two Burunjis going over to the foot of the cliff and scaling laboriously up it, pretending that he had a rifle slung over his shoulder. At the top he lost his grip and fell back into the runnel. I could almost hear the screams of the original white man, as I watched the Burunji re-enact the scene of his dropping to the ground with his legs doubled up under him. Then the leader walked across to the fallen man, pointed an imaginary rifle at him and again what sounded like a shot reverberated from the cliffs.

The next scene of the corroboree showed that the other white man had been sent up the cliff and succeeded in going through the cleft. As Tajalli later told me, he must have panicked in the silent darkness when he reached the barrier at the entrance to the cave, then in darkness because the initiation fire had been put out. Tajalli explained that the man had run back to the cleft.

The final act of the drama was played out when the man reappeared in the cleft and stood there pleading to the man below before he collapsed face down with his head at the cleft entrance, as the leader shot him. Even the sound of the dead man's rifle falling down the cliff was vividly reproduced, and then we saw what happened to it as the leader mimed the action of picking it up and throwing it far out into the swamp.

And so we came to the end of that remarkable story which the Aborigines had reconstructed, down to the minutest detail, from the interpretation of tracks and signs of what they knew had taken place at that fateful spot beyond the Gumrai-Gumrai.

But the end of the corroboree did not mean that the rituals were over.

The Burunjis fed the fires until the flames roared, lighting up the cliff face even more brightly than before.

Then they gathered around Kammaluk, kneeling on the ground in a semicircle between the fires facing Tajalli, Tajurra and me in the dinghy. Kammaluk had the woven human-hair bag resting on his shield across his knees. The two grass tubes were lying on the ground behind him, the one with the looped handle holding the dry grass sticks he had made earlier in the day.

The Burunjis sat staring anxiously at their leader as he picked up the bag, loosened the draw-string and then bent forward to tip the bag's contents on to the ground in front of him. They all then bent over eagerly to see how the contents of the bag had fallen and what could be read in the pattern of clearly discernible witchcraft they had outlined.

I stood up and stared intently from the dinghy. So did Tajalli and Tajurra, and we all saw the assortment of teji stones, mummified lizards and the other sacred objects now lying in full view on the ground . . . And there in the centre of them lay that glistening black pearl—bigger than a pigeon's egg!

Kammaluk's "wah!" of jubilation at the result of his appeal to their god Burunji was taken up by the others as he quickly scooped the objects back into their bag, drew the draw-string tight and hung the bag's cord around his neck to let the bag hang down his chest. Then he put the shield face up on the ground, jumped up and grabbed the tube of grass sticks, and put the looped handle around his neck so that the tube hung down behind him. Then he took a glowing fire-stick from the corroboree fire, stuck the unlighted end in his mouth and ran to the base of the cliff. In one bound he cleared the runnel and began the climb up to the cleft. In the glaring light from the fires he seemed to merge into the blackness of the cliff until he reached and clambered through the cleft into the tunnel. It was not until he turned to drop the tube on the tunnel floor that he became clearly visible because of the white-striped corroboree markings all over him. But he remained there only long enough to take the grass sticks from the tube, light one by holding it to the fire-stick and blow the stick into a flaming torch. Then, carrying the torch in one hand and the rest in the other, he vanished into the tunnel, leaving a faint flickering of his going in the cleft until only the dancing firelight's glare remained on the wall of the cliff.

The Burunjis sat there talking among themselves and watching the cleft.

Tajalli then explained to me that Kammaluk's bravery in going into the tunnel at night was proof to his god that the Burunji leader had atoned for his past mistakes. It was now safe to perform the final act of cleansing the taboo he and the elders had invoked long ago to prevent anyone, white or black, from ever again entering the secret initiation caves unless, *as a further protection for themselves*, an honest white man could be found who would listen and learn the truth of what had happened to the Burunji people. Thus the way would be opened for the final act of tribal justice to be carried out by catching that Aboriginal man who had murdered Turrapini, and inflicting on him the supreme punishment of his tribe—being "sung" to death in the dreaded ceremony of the Pointing of the Bone.

And so the fact of my being white with red hair and that it was I who had found the Burunjis' message stick had made me one of the pieces that completed the jig-saw of events long past and events still to come.

However, sitting in the dinghy just waiting proved too much for me. I fell asleep.

IO

My dozing off was interrupted by Tajurra shaking me awake with a hissing whisper of "Jimmy! Jimmy! Come on!"

I woke to find him standing outside the dinghy, still urging me to "Come on!" I stood up and looked around. Tajalli was at the cooking fire arranging the tortoises in the bed of live coals he had levelled out at the edge of the still roaring fire. I could see the file snake coiled in the coals where he had put it.

The Burunjis were at the water's edge washing away their ceremonial body paint, Kammaluk among them. I got out of the dinghy and went with Tajurra to put on the billies of potatoes and onions, with the tea billy alongside them. Tajalli, who had finished his job of getting the snake and tortoises cooking, smiled at me and said, "Everybody happy now, Jimmy. Debbil-debbils finish longa there now." He pointed up at the cleft to show me that the skull was no longer there.

"Where that white fella bones now?" I asked, and he pointed to the two tubes lying at the base of the cliff.

"Kammaluk bring that one down longa grass bag; put other one longa other bag."

"What for?" I enquired but got no immediate answer because Kammaluk and the elders came crowding round us at the cooking fire in a chattering, excited band. Kammaluk said something to Tajalli who translated it to me: "Jimmy, Burunji men by and by give you something longa their camp. Kammaluk want you eat little fella bit snake, little fella bit terebee (he meant tortoise) when 'im cook. You tell

125

Kammaluk *sibba*, eh?"

For a moment or so I hesitated until I saw Kammaluk, who was standing beside me anxiously waiting for my answer. Then I said, *"Sibba!"*

Kammaluk then put his hands on my shoulders to grip me in pleasure at my acceptance of what was really an invitation to sit in on the traditional post-initiation "banquet" which always follows the ceremony of tribal acceptance of anyone who has passed the test of the elders to become a worthwhile man of their tribe; evidently I had. Kammaluk's stream of talk that followed, as he addressed us all, saved me from embarrassment because I could not understand him; but Tajalli and Tajurra could, as was clear from their own excited chatter and *"Sibba"*'s of approval. When I asked Tajurra what was being said, he grinned and answered, "By and by, you find out."

And so everybody sat down to talk while the billies of potatoes and onions began to bubble and the aroma of the baking snake and tortoises wafted around us.

Now that the curse of their great god Burunji had been exorcised from their secret inner cave, the Burunjis were no longer under the taboo of silence about what had taken place through the insane acts of that surviving white man after he had shot the other two white men and was left alone with Turrapini. So Tajalli was free to tell Tajurra and me, in brief, what happened then. While Tajurra cast an occasional eye on the cooking we were told how Kammaluk had kept the initiation party of elders and boys back in the big cave where they waited. They had heard the shooting in the morning that had killed the two white men but thought it meant that the two Burunji women had been shot. So the party waited until the sun was directly over the shaft leading up to the rain forest and sent down to the big cave a dim green twilight. In that dim glow Kammaluk took his sacred shield and woven human-hair bag of sacred objects and put them on the rock ledge in the secret inner cave and retreated back to the elders and newly initiated young men at the barrier. That done, the whole party formed a semicircle facing the secret inner chamber and there, in the twilight, Kammaluk, flanked by the elders and newly initiated young men, invoked the curse: that no man, black or white, would ever reach that secret chamber and live to tell of it, unless . . . At that point, Tajalli looked intently at me and my red hair and said, "Kammaluk and Burunji men happy now, Jimmy. He know you honest white man; you close up longa Burunji god now." It was dreadfully embarrassing for me to be told that.

But my embarrassment was short-lived because Tajurra got up at that point to check the cooking. When he came back, Tajalli resumed the story to explain how the initiation party had waited in the big cave until late in the afternoon when it was decided that Kammaluk be sent out to reconnoitre. So he made his way up to the cleft and found the body of the white man where it had fallen.

On looking down at the scene below he saw first the body of the dead woman lying by the smouldering fire. Looking down the cliff he then saw the body of the other white man lying in the runnel. Even at that height and distance, Kammaluk could plainly read the tracks of the surviving white man where they led into the swamp with Turrapini's tracks ahead, showing that he was using her as a hostage to lead him to safety. Out in the swamp there was no sign of either, which was not surprising because of the dense, head-high swamp grass.

And so Kammaluk called the rest of the elders and young men up to the cleft and the party descended the cliff to the ground below to read the whole damning story in the tracks of that surviving white man's murderous rampage—for nothing!

Then, left without food (the white man and Turrapini had taken all the available food with them), and no spears with which to catch more for themselves, the Burunjis were forced to wait out the night before leaving at daybreak the next morning, towing the body of the dead woman on a makeshift raft of timber they had fashioned from what they had been able to gather along the base of the cliff. Burunji custom demanded that the dead Burunji woman be given a tree burial at the other side of the swamp.

That journey, as Tajalli told it, was indeed a nightmare, especially for Kammaluk, whose bullet wound in the shoulder began to make it well-nigh impossible for him to do anything else but lead his party back across the Gumrai-Gumrai. He knew the rest of the tribe would have returned post-haste from their Walkabout back to their main camp when the initiation party failed to show up at the arranged meeting-place in the ranges above the basalt cliffs where the secret caves are.

At that junction of the story, Tajalli got up to help Tajurra take the cooked food off the fire. He then said to me, "Get salt, Jimmy, get dish. We soon eat good fella tucker."

Tajurra helped me bring the salt, dish and other things from the dinghy. We put them on the ground in the centre of the circle of men. Tajalli took the billies of spuds and onions, eased their lids to drain off the water and dumped the spuds and onions into the dish alongside the cooked snake and the tortoises. Then he made a big billy of sweetened black tea and sat down between Tajurra and me again.

And so, according to Burunji custom, they started that meal and began by pulling apart the baked snake to reveal its snow-white flesh. Then Kammaluk said something across the circle to Tajalli, who said, "All right, Jimmy, you want 'im piece?" and pulled the still piping-hot meat over so that I could take a piece and drop it on my plate. With all eyes

128

watching I took a pinch of salt from the open tin before me and sprinkled it over the hot meat . . . Then, gingerly, I stuck a fork into it, lifted the portion to my mouth to taste it . . . Hunger, they say, is the best sauce for any food; but hunger notwithstanding, that mouthful convinced me that eating file snake baked in its skin is an experience any gourmet would delight in. That tender white meat tasted like something between chicken and veal; a shout of laughter rang out as the group watched the pleasure with which I chewed and swallowed my first-ever snake, cooked in the coals. Then we all tucked in to the feast.

Once over my initial hesitancy about eating the unfamiliar, it was a simple matter of progress like the others to a baked tortoise suitably salted. Perhaps the sight of those black feet drawn into the shell in the shrinking of the cooking did deter me a little until I pulled one, sprinkled a little salt on it and . . . it was tender and full of flavour—like turtle meat but with an extra taste like rich oily Queensland nuts, made more delicious by our adding to each mouthful a helping of the spuds and onions. And so the feast ended with the drinking from the billy of sweet black tea to wash everything down into bellies full and satisfied at last. The empty shells were tossed into the cooking fire to burn in the coals.

Tajalli took a burning stick from the flames, lit the pipe, and threw the stick back into the fire. He took a few puffs and handed the pipe across for Kammaluk's pleasure and so on round the circle of men, except Tajurra and me, and so back to Tajalli who put his palm over the bowl to put out the burning tobacco and stuck the pipe back in to the belt of his lap-lap.

Then both Kammaluk and Tajalli got up and stoked the cooking fire with more logs. That done, Kammaluk walked towards the foot of the cliff, throwing a huge silhouette of himself up on to the rock face as he approached. The shadow grew smaller until he bent and picked up the two tubes filled with the bones of the white men and returned to the left-hand fire to throw them into it with an exclamation of "Wah!" that was taken up by the other Burunjis as they sprang to their feet. The echoes of "Wah! Wah! Wah!" reverberated along the cliffs as the men began piling wood on top of the tubes until they had a roaring bonfire. Then they stepped back into the space between the fires to await Kammaluk's next move.

To my amazement, Kammaluk cupped his hands to his mouth and, facing the cliff to look up at the distant fringe of the encircling rain forest, he called out, "Yarragul! ... Yarragul! ... Yarragul! ..."

He paused between each call as though he expected to hear an answer, but only the ricochet of the echoes came back until finally even they faded away into the empyrean darkness and the mourning of the wind carrying the howling of the scrub dingoes and the endless "tap, tap, tap tap tap" of the coffin birds.

A sudden ghastly feeling of impending doom swept over me. As though a moving picture had penetrated my mind I saw my mother, lying on her bed, deathly pale and ill. I saw her in her nightgown get up and open the medicine cabinet and take out a bottle of something ... The picture faded, leaving me shocked and terrified ... I knew with absolute certainty that she was having another of those recurring bouts of sickness. And I also knew that the sound of the name Yarragul that had been shouted at the cliffs by Kammaluk was the cause of my vision. So intense was my dread, I could only stare blankly at the roaring fire consuming the bones. Time stood still.

I came back to reality to find Tajalli seated beside me and shaking me. He gasped, "Jimmy! What for you look sick?"

For the life of me I could not tell him why. I could only

look helplessly at poor Tajurra seated at the other side of Tajalli with his gaze fixed on me in as helpless a stare as my own. And there, all around us, the circle of the Burunjis watched in silence. Tajalli, to break the uneasy atmosphere that hung over us all, then spoke across the circle to Kammaluk who nodded and said something to the other Burunjis. Then they all lay down on the ground in a row between the fires and prepared to go to sleep.

Tajalli then told Tajurra and me to get our blanket rolls from the dinghy and take our allotted places alongside the Burunjis. We laid our blankets out, Tajurra next to the last Burunji man in the row, mine next in the line, with a space left for Tajalli, who had got up and was staring into the wind-blown coals of the funeral fire.

In the brooding silence I lay there listening to the mournful sound of the wind carrying the message of all the other sounds of the night. Gradually sleep took over the camp and I listened for some time to Tajurra and the others as their heavy breathing indicated their deepening retreat into oblivion and forgetfulness of the brooding fears of that night.

For me, sleep would not come, nor for Tajalli who was still standing silent and motionless by the wind-blown fire.

In my agony of mind I got up, holding the blanket around me, and went to stand by him. He just looked at me and motioned me to sit down with him by the fire.

There, in whispers, we began to talk. He started by asking again why I had panicked after hearing the name Yarragul.

I avoided telling him that I had lied that day under the pandanus palms when he asked me if my mother had seen that cursed message stick. In my stupidity, I knew that the evil force within that carved stick had entered my mother's mind, but I wanted to go on believing that its influence would eventually fade away of its own accord and leave her freed from its threat of eventual, certain death by the decree of the great dolphin god Burunji.

To deflect Tajalli away from gazing at me, I said, "What for Kammaluk sing out 'Yarragul' longa cliffs, Tajalli?"

In a hushed whisper, to avoid disturbing the sleeping men, he answered, "Yarragul, Burunji man, kill 'im sister belonga me, Jimmy."

And so, now that the name of the wanted man could be freely spoken, Tajalli could tell me what took place on that morning before the Burunji initiation party set out to cross the Gumrai-Gumrai and give the dead woman a proper tree burial before continuing on to the Burunjis' main camp.

Tajalli said the elders knew that the mad white man could get overland to the nearest white homestead of Oonaderra by making Turrapini show him the way by the long circuitous route through the alternating open forests and rain forests which, for centuries, the two tribes had used as their common route in their comings and goings when visiting each other. So the Burunji elders decided to select the fittest, fastest man among them: that man was Yarragul. He was intructed to proceed ahead of the initiation party and get to the main camp without delay. There he was to instruct old Bennatuk, the Burunji tribal carver of sacred shields, to carve the message stick that was to alert the Oona tribe to intercept the mad white man and kill him.

At that point my curiosity overcame my uneasy feelings about my mother, enough to make me whisper to ask why Yarragul did not catch up with the white man and kill him.

Tajalli shook his head and whispered, "No, Jimmy." He then explained that whenever the two tribes have a reason for entering the other's tribal territory they cannot carry weapons of any sort—they must be given special permission by the other tribe to do so. Any killing of anything on the other's land is taboo, that is the sole prerogative of the tribal owners of the territory. Tajalli further explained that any food growing on either tribe's land was free for all to gather and eat. The significance of that piece of information came to me later.

Continuing, Tajalli said that the initiation party reached the other side of the swamp and found the tracks of Turrapini and the white man showing where they had eaten and slept before continuing their journey on to Oonaderra. Tajalli said the white man's tracks clearly showed that he was also physically ill.

The initiation party, Tajalli said, was able to fashion makeshift spears to catch enough barramundi to tide them over till the next morning when they found a suitable tree and the dead Burunji woman was buried according to tribal custom. The party then set off for the main camp. And at the junction where the side creek branches off from the main creek they met Yarragul carrying the message stick hanging from his neck with a paperbark cover wrapped around it to prevent the eyes of the uninitiated or of women from seeing it. After a brief exchange with the men and boys Yarragul sped on his way to try to reach Oonaderra ahead of the white man. The party continued on back to the main camp.

Huddled in my blanket, I waited for Tajalli to go on, but he was staring into the gleaming red coals of the wind-blown fire, apparently lost in reverie. He was so engrossed in his thoughts that he seemed completely oblivious of my presence. His head, outlined in the red glow of the firelight, with his mane of greying hair held back by his woven human-hair headband, gave him a peculiarly god-like look of stern dignity; yet his black face and deep-set eyes still conveyed the deep humility and compassion of the man.

Suddenly he whispered to himself, "Myee Wundul! ... Myee Wundul! ... Myee Turrapini!"

He was invoking the spirit of his dead sister whose bones lay hidden in that stringybark tree on Oonaderra.

133

I glanced over my shoulder and saw that the moon rising over the Gumrai-Gumrai had created a golden aura of moonlight above the swamp grass swaying in the ghostly mourning wind. I touched him on the shoulder and whispered "Look". But I could not make him look away from the protective circle of the firelight because of the debbil-debbils he believed there to be outside the sanctuary of his night fire.

But my breaking of his reverie prompted him to go on with the telling of what had eventually happened to his sister. Still in a whisper, he said, "That bad fella Yarragul follow tracks belonga white man, belonga Turrapini; two day 'im run fast; by and by 'im see tracks stop longa creek longa Oonaderra; white man, Turrapini camp longa creek before sun go down; Yarragul see 'im eat finger cherry longa bushes longa creek."

Suddenly the reason for the partial blindness of the white man, which Tajalli had mentioned to my mother and me, became quite clear—he was suffering the toxic effects of the dangerous fungus that develops on the cherries during the intense heat and humidity of the Wet Season; the end result is always incurable blindness for whoever eats them.

Tajalli said they learned the whole story when he and Trokka, one of the Oona elders, examined the tracks and signs left all around the place where the finger cherries were growing a mile or so up the creek from Cannon Ball Rock. He told me Yarragul camped some distance away from the white man and Turrapini to wait for the morning and the onset of the first stages of blindness in the white man who was also ill from the effects of the scrub fever that was making him shake and chatter madly in the delirium of that tropical disease . . .

The following morning at sunrise Yarragul called out to Turrapini, who was preparing to go on with the white man, to tell her to lead him into the ranges and lose him so that

134

Yarragul could get to the Oonas' camp with his message stick to alert the elders to catch and kill the white man.

Then Yarragul, Tajalli said, let her go on with the white man but she, ignoring Yarragul's orders, allowed her pity and compassion to rule her head—she continued along the track that leads to the Oonas' camp and the Brents' homestead, supporting the stumbling man all the way.

Enraged by what she was doing, Yarragul waited to make certain that she *was* taking him in that direction. Then, in a mad fury of murderous rage, he raced after the pair and caught up with them at Cannon Ball Rock.

Tajalli paused, which gave me the opportunity to ask how he could possibly know all that had happened. He said, "Me work, Trokka work longa saddle-shed longa home paddock fix 'im saddles. Me hear big fella scream; look out longa window, longa Cannon Ball Rock, see Yarragul fight Turrapini. Grandfather see fight too, 'im ride horse longa west gate; gallop over longa Cannon Ball Rock. Before 'im get there, Yarragul break neck belonga Turrapini; she fall longa ground; Yarragul look, see grandfather come; he run like mad fella back longa track; no more see 'im no more. Grandfather put white man longa horse take 'im longa house."

All impatience, I waited for him to resume. He told me how he and Trokka ran the half mile or so to the Rock to find Turrapini lying paralysed but still alive—clutched in her right hand was the paperbark cover belonging to the message stick. There was no sign of the stick itself.

And so the strange working of destiny in our lives was carried out that morning when my grandfather, almost as if he had been guided to the scene, had ridden to the home paddock's west gate to become a participant in the drama that was to make another sad chapter in the lives of the Aborigines and the Brents.

The sight of poor old Tajalli recalling those events was

made more poignant for me when I saw the tears running down his face as he re-lived the final scene of the death of his only sister. He said Turrapini was able to talk to him for a little while until he tried to help her to sit up. The moment he did that her head rolled helplessly, her spinal cord snapped and she was dead. After that her body was put in the big stringybark to await the catching of Yarragul to begin the ceremony of the lifting of the taboo so that the bones could be re-interred in a tree on Burunji territory.

I only sought one more answer by asking Tajalli if my grandfather had tried to help Turrapini in any way.

"No, Jimmy," he answered. "Grandfather belonga you not like black people. All the time 'im say black people boongs, all the time 'im say pig nice thing; want to kill all the black people feed longa pigs; 'im say 'im Christian, 'im say God like white fella people, not like black people."

He got to his feet, a clear indication that he no longer wanted to go on talking about a subject that had already caused too much heartache and racial bitterness. He asked me to get the self-raising flour and salt from the dinghy so that he could make dampers for breakfast the next morning. I got the things from the dinghy and lay down again near Tajurra.

In the whirl of emotions and anxiety that had been stirred in my mind I lay there listening to the eerie sound of the crying wind that evoked in me, in my state of acute imaginings, a feeling that I was being held in the stillness of the eye of an emotional cyclone while all around the debbil-debbils were flying in an ever-lessening circle in preparation for the final destructive blast of vengeance still to come. Even so, I was spared a totally sleepless night. The sight of Tajalli preparing the dampers brought me a sense of peace ... I slipped over the brink of that night into oblivion.

I was aroused by Tajalli shaking Tajurra and me. "Come on,

sun come up."

We sat up to find the grinning Burunjis squatting around us with a billy of steaming tea and the two big dampers that Tajalli had made resting on a slab of bark in the centre of the circle.

Tajalli asked, "Me open one fella tin corn beef, Jimmy, eh?"

I nodded, still half asleep, and he went and opened a tin in the dinghy. He squatted down beside Tajurra and me, sliced one of the dampers into nine thick slices and then smeared each with an equal ration of the corned beef and handed them around. And so breakfast was eaten, the tea drunk, and then the other damper and stores were loaded into the dinghy with two billies of tea, firmly lidded down, to provide us with refreshment as we traversed the Gumrai-Gumrai. The journey began as soon as everything around the camp site had been checked and the fires doused.

Tajurra and I piled our blankets aboard while the camp inspection was carried out by the others. I saw that the dinghy rope was securely spliced back into its bow ring as well as back on to the anchor. Kammaluk's shield and his bag of sacred tribal objects were safe in the dinghy under a blanket.

Finally the Burunjis, Tajalli with them, set off into the swamp, carrying their three-pronged spears, more, I believe, as a ritualistic gesture than for use on the journey.

Tajurra and I, barefooted, were at the bow of the dinghy and at Tajalli's order to "Come on" we began the weary trek back over the dreaded Gumrai-Gumrai swamp.

It would be pointless to recount that exhausting return journey; suffice to say, we made it without serious incident to our first camp where we repeated the catching of barramundi for that night's meal. Rather than go on holding my guilty secret of the lies I had told about my mother not having seen that cursed message stick, I waited until after we had eaten and then confided to Tajalli and Tajurra, in a whisper, my fears about my mother's recurring bouts of sickness. Seated there between the blazing fires with father and son on either side of me, I was taken aback by their shocked reaction when I told them that my mother *had* seen the message stick.

Tajalli gasped, "You plurry fool, Jimmy!" and Tajurra was equally shocked. "Jimmy, what for you tell lie longa me?"

I could only hang my head in mingled shame and apprehension at what I had done. Then I looked up to see the Burunjis staring at me. Kammaluk snapped a brief question at Tajalli whose tense, strained expression, when I glanced up at him, clearly indicated the terror he felt at what I had told him. Before he answered Kammaluk, he said to me, "Jimmy, you go there." He pointed to the far right-hand side of the fires. "You sit there longa fire; by and by me speak longa you."

I made no protest. I just got up and sat by the fire away from them. Across the roaring fire I could see but not hear the men in tense debate.

Suddenly Tajalli spoke to Tajurra who got up and came around to me. He sat down, looked desperately at me and said, almost in tears, "Jimmy, what for you tell lie longa me, longa Tajalli?"

As best I could, I tried to convince him that my own desperate fears for my mother's welfare had led me to hope that she would get well again when all the fuss over the message stick was cleared up after the secret corroboree had been held to exorcise the debbil-debbils from the Burunjis' sacred initiation caves. I told him that I really believed the lifting of that curse the Burunjis had invoked through their god would also remove the deadly influence of the message stick's power over the uninitiated or any woman unfortunate enough to set eyes on it.

His answer was instantaneous: "No, Jimmy, that bad fella stick keep bad fella debbil-debbil longa 'im all the time. Suppose 'im wrong fella people see that stick, maybe 'im die quick like Turrapini; maybe ..." He stopped, seeing the effect his halting words had on me.

My "Please, Tajurra, what for you stop?" got the answer I dreaded. He began to sob and cry and through his sobs he said, "Me no want mother belonga you die, Jimmy; me want old men tell Kammaluk, tell Tajalli talk longa Burunji god, talk longa Oona god, ask 'im not let mother belonga you die by and by."

Hope, desperate hope sprang in me. I said, "You think maybe old men longa Burunjis, old men longa Oona people stop mother belonga me die, Tajurra?"

Still crying, he shrugged and said, "Burunji people, Oona people, all kind people, Jimmy. Tajalli and Kammaluk soon know what old men tell 'im do."

And so poor Tajurra and stupid lying me were also made to go on suffering for a multiple crime that we had had no part in.

After the debate had gone on for some time, Tajalli called Tajurra back to the group and Tajalli came over and sat with me. He was no longer angry: only an expression of deep worry and apprehension showed in his sad face when he said, "Maybe you not silly fella boy, Jimmy; me know you get big fella worry longa mother belonga you. Me think you know about Burunji talk stick make people die, sometimes altogether quick, sometimes little bit before, some people, maybe woman, die too, eh?"

He had guessed from my previous admission that I had known all along about the stick's deadly influence. But he had wisely made his statement without letting me know that he had also guessed who I had got the information from.

I heaved a sigh of relief when I realized that my friend

Tajurra was to be spared from any punishment. But still I wanted to know where the message stick was and why it should not be destroyed to prevent it causing any further trouble.

Tajalli just looked intently at me and said, "Jimmy, that bad fella Yarragul die first before that bad fella stick stop bad things altogether."

"What for that man die first?" I asked.

Then he explained that, because the killing of his sister had taken place on Oona tribal ground, the killer, Yarragul, must be sung to death by the Oona elders on Oona territory. Once that had been accomplished, the Burunji elders would have their god remove the deadly influence of the message stick which would then be destroyed and all its power with it. The message stick, he said, was being held by the Burunji tribal carver Bennatuk, now an old man, the same man who had carved the stick in the long ago.

Tajalli stood up then and said, "More better you go sleep now, Jimmy. By and by longa morning we go longa Burunji camp. Kammaluk want give you good fella thing longa Burunji people: Burunji people want see you longa camp. All right, eh?"

I nodded, wondering what on earth he was talking about, but I refrained from my usual sticky-beak inquisitiveness of wanting to know the what-when-where-and-why of everything immediately, and walked back with him to the group already settling down for the night to sleep. He and I took our places in the line ... For some time I lay listening to the soughing of the wind over the Gumrai-Gumrai, crying like a lost soul for sanctuary from a world without conscience for what had been done to an innocent people by order of a ruthless white man who had been helped to side-step justice while another man, Yarragul, was now called upon to face a tribal death penalty for the lesser crime that he had committed in the killing of one woman, Turrapini.

I must confess that I was also anxious for the welfare of my mother ... What if that man roaming the ranges did not respond to the call to give himself up to the Oonas ... What then?

But I resolutely thrust that frightening possibility out of my thoughts and somehow managed to slip beneath my fears and got to sleep.

What a difference it made to the last stage of our return journey to the Burunji main camp to have the flow of the two streams with us instead of having to progress against them.

With Tajalli travelling on the banks with the Burunjis, and Tajurra and me having little more to do than hold on to the bow of the dinghy as we towed it along the longer, shallow side creek, we set off that morning, everybody anxious to get to the camp as early as possible and Tajalli, Tajurra and myself more than eager to get back to our own territory on Oonaderra.

Yet how strange it was for me to pass into and through the rain forest and to experience the sudden silence as the sound of the Gumrai-Gumrai wind was abruptly shut out behind us. But, also, what a blessed relief to be gone from it. Nothing would ever induce me to cross that dreadful swamp again. That we had accomplished our mission of retrieving the Burunji shield and the sacred objects for Kammaluk and the elders, and thus lifted the twenty-five-year-old curse from their sacred caves, was reason enough for me never to want to undergo another such ordeal again.

However, with that ordeal behind us, we made an uneventful return to the main camp where we anchored on the bank leading up fom the creek at the top of which Tajalli was standing and beckoning to us. He called out, "Jimmy! You bring 'im shield and that fella bag tied longa 'im, eh?"

"OK." I got the shield with Kammaluk's bag tied to the back of it and followed Tajurra up to Tajalli. I wanted to hand him the shield but he said, "No, Jimmy—you come longa me, bring 'im shield."

It was then that I saw the centre of the camp thronged by the entire tribe squatting in a semicircle, facing us across a roaring fire. It was so early in the afternoon, I was surprised to see the tribespeople there at all, until Tajurra whispered to me, "Kammaluk tell people about you; by and by 'im give you something."

I didn't stop to ask him what, because, as we approached the fire, a loud "Wah!" greeted us from the assembled crowd. Tajalli led the way around the fire, and as he did he whispered, "Keep that fella shield up, Jimmy; no more put 'im longa ground."

"OK," I said, and we stopped in front of the fire to face the people ... Then, to my surprise and embarrassment, Tajalli and Tajurra deserted me and vanished into the crowd. I stood holding the shield and bag cradled in my arms.

The weight of that shield was something I couldn't manage for too long; fortunately Tajalli and Kammaluk soon came hurrying through the squatting crowd towards me. An eager chattering broke out among the tribespeople.

Thankfully I handed Kammaluk his shield, and he positioned himself on my right, letting the tip of his shield rest on the ground. Tajalli ranged himself on my left and whispered, "No more get fright, Jimmy; Kammaluk want tell Burunji people about you; 'im tell 'im you good fella white man; want make you all the same man belonga Burunji tribe. All right, eh?"

I nodded, and he spoke to Kammaluk.

Then Kammaluk raised his left hand. The crowd grew silent as he began to address them in rapid Burunji. For perhaps five minutes he talked, and then he raised his voice to ask them, "White fella Jimmy—Burunji? *Sibba?*"

An instant roar of "*Sibba! Sibba! Sibba!*" gave him his answer. He then called out, "Bennatuk!"

An old, old man, who reminded me of Trokka, stepped from the crowd carrying something in his cupped, out-stretched hands. He came and stood in front of us, looking intently at me and my bare red-haired head. He said softly, "*Sibba, sibba,*" as he opened his hands to show what they held: it was a woven human-hair ceremonial headband adorned with two fringes that hang over the ears to mark the wearer as a tribal member without blemish in the eyes of the elders.

He placed the band on my head and adjusted it, repeating "*Sibba, sibba.*" His voice was almost drowned in the shouting and yelling that broke out among the people, jubilant at the turn of events that obviously meant so much to them. As for me, well, I did feel that my being made an honorary member of their tribe was very special, but I still feel I was awarded more than I deserved when the real achievement had been won by others.

As the shouting went on, Kammaluk again raised his hand in a sweeping movement to signal the end of the proceedings. The people began to disperse in a frenzy of more shouting and merriment as they swarmed around us. But Kammaluk, carrying his shield, strode through the crowd to his mia-mia, obviously to hide away the shield and precious bag.

Tajalli nudged me to get away from the roaring fire, and he then hurried after the Burunji leader while I, wearing my headband, moved through the crowd in search of Tajurra, whom I found talking to Monabi and Carawul, the two young Oona women who had undergone the pirralulla ritual on Oonaderra to become women of the Burunji tribe. They were standing on the edge of the crowd, obviously very happy at seeing Tajurra again; but their greeting of "'Lo, Jimmy; you Burunji fella now, eh?" was brief because they had to join the other women around the fire preparing a feast of celebration, which, as Tajurra explained to me, was to be a "Big fella tucker time, all the same one we have longa Oonaderra, when we say goodbye longa Monabi, longa Carawul."

And so it eventually proved to be when, a couple of hours later, we sat down in family groups to gorge on baked wallaby, yams and something else I had never eaten before—baked cabbage palm tops. Stripped of fronds, the long tubular palm sheaths encasing the tender inner core were baked in the coals; when they were pulled out and split open with a tomahawk, there was the inner core ready to eat with the wallaby, the baked fish, big pearl shell oysters in their shells, and yugari shell-fish.

The most surprising thing of all was for me to be invited into Kammaluk's family group along with Tajalli and Tajurra. We were served by Kammaluk's woman—none other than Monabi herself—who squatted with us to share the coolamon of steaming goodies she had helped prepare with the other women.

As we sat there chattering, laughing and enjoying the "good fella tucker" of our hosts, I could not help wondering if Monabi, under her cheerful expression, felt homesick for Oonaderra, so I asked her. She, chewing a mouthful of the hot food, swallowed it, giggled and said, "No more cry about Oonaderra now, Jimmy; by and by we all go Walkabout, see all Oona people again. Kammaluk good fella man, 'im make me good fella woman by and by. That true, Jimmy," she assured me, and I knew she meant it. She was really happy to be Kammaluk's woman, and why not?

And so the feast ran its course to the moment when the sun was setting and Tajalli got up and spoke to Kammaluk who got up, too, with the rest of us and wished us goodbye in the Burunji tongue. Then Tajalli told Tajurra and me to go down to the dinghy and wait for him. We nodded, said goodbye to Monabi and made our way across and down the bank and got into the dinghy. Tajurra took his seat at the oars, more to show me, I think, that notwithstanding my headband, he still was equal to me in all other respects. But I just could not resist quipping him about my new-found status by telling him, "Me big fella Burunji man now," and flexing my arms to prove it.

He just grinned and retorted, "All right! You no more be big fella Burunji man when we get back longa Oonaderra; mother belonga you belt you longa head, tell 'im you shut up! She no like big fella skite like you!"

I grinned in reply, shrugged and let it go because Tajalli, once more in his khaki rig-out, was on his way down the bank with his lap-lap and headband inside his shirt, bulging it out front.

He stepped into the bow with the rope and anchor and said, "All right, Tajurra, we go now." And so we rowed on downstream and passed the Burunjis gathered on the beach to wave us goodbye as we rowed past.

Yes, I was happy for us to receive such a send-off, but not half as happy as I felt when I caught sight of the *Curlew* riding high in the water at her anchor.

And the feeling when we stepped on board was akin to what an exile must feel like returning home. At least that was how I felt as we began the stowing away of the things from the dinghy before settling down for the night in preparation for what Tajalli called "piccaninny daylight" when we would make our early departure for Oonaderra.

II

Morning dawned, a typical Cape York dawn of sun and sea merging into a blood-red iridescence of colours, as Tajalli hauled in the anchor and I, in the steering seat, started the motor and we swung south to pick up speed for the journey back to Oonaderra. Tajurra, munching a treacle-smeared pufftaloon, came and stood beside me with a mug of tea in his hand and said, "Me steer 'im boat by and by, Jimmy?"

"OK," I answered. "You wash dishes, me give you seat, you take wheel."

He finished the tea and the 'loon and soon had the galley clean and tidied up. All the while he had been busy I had watched Tajalli, who sat up front on the hatch-cover with his precious blanket roll, now containing his lap-lap and all-important headband, tucked away behind his heels for safe keeping. It was plain to see that he was deeply troubled about what the future might hold in store for his people . . . and I knew that my confession of two nights before was the main cause of his worries because of what could happen to my mother if that man roaming the ranges failed to obey the summons of his god to present himself on Oona territory for the expiation of his crime by the inexorable death penalty of tribal retribution.

Then Tajurra came up to me and asked, "OK now, Jimmy?"

I nodded and left my seat. He clambered into it, took the wheel and looked at the quadrant lever which was above the three-quarter speed mark. We were doing a good eight knots an hour. "Me keep 'im that fella thing all the time like that?" he asked and I told him yes—I wanted to get home to my mother regardless of her warning when we left Oonaderra to keep the boat at a steady six knots.

He just shrugged. I went to sit with Tajalli who seemed unwilling to answer my questions about what was worrying him. We sat there for quite a while until I got up fed up with his avoiding any talk of the future that held for me as much anxiety and apprehension as it did for him and his people as well as the Burunjis.

I was on the point of getting up to leave him, when he said, "Jimmy, me got big fella worry altogether now. Me tell mother belonga you me bring that bad fella talk stick back, give 'im back longa her. Suppose she ask you about that stick not come back longa me; by and by mother belonga you say me big fella liar?"

And so I found out that in his eyes, his reputation was at stake because of what he had inadvertently promised my mother he would do about bringing the stick back.

For my part, I never wanted to see it again. It was the cause of all our troubles which began on the day I found the cursed thing and the log-book hidden away in the false bottom of my grandfather's old tin trunk.

I told him that he need not worry about keeping his promise to my mother because I would stall any questions she might ask about the stick not being returned to her. But saying this and giving him a further example of my conceited belief in my ability to hoodwink my mother, did not impress him at all. He just looked at me patiently and said, "More better you no more tell lies longa mother belonga you, Jimmy. Maybe by and by me fix 'im up something about that bad fella stick."

And there the matter had to rest. And so impressed was I by the man I had come to respect as my own father that I inwardly vowed never to do anything ever again that might cause him or my mother or indeed anyone at all to suffer because of my inexperience and lack of common sense in matters that I could not handle by myself.

I left him and spent the rest of the trip with Tajurra, who steered all the way till we reached the channel through the reef where I took over and headed the *Curlew* through and around to the anchorage fronting the house.

We dropped anchor and rowed ashore. With only a quick exchange of "So longs", Tajalli and Tajurra, each clasping his bed-roll, ran along the beach heading for the camp and whatever else awaited them there ...

I walked up the slope and when I reached the top I saw my mother standing on the front veranda steps over at the house. My spirits sank ... she was in her bright yellow dressing-gown and even at that distance I could see the effect of her recurring sickness on her face and body.

I literally raced across to the house and up the front steps to take her in my arms. After giving her a hug and kiss, I let her go and said, "Gee, Mum, what's the matter? You look really ill and worn out."

"Oh, now, now," she answered, putting on a wan little smile in an attempt to stop me noticing her all too obvious wasting away of body and health. "Did you miss me over the past week?" she asked.

"Yes, of course I did, Mum," I answered and added, "Did you miss me?"

She again smiled a wan smile and answered jokingly, "Well, I like that! Why should I have missed you? You go gallivanting all over the place with not a care in the world. What do you think your poor old mum did, left here all alone?"

"Gee, sorry Mum. I didn't think you'd miss me that much," I apologized, but she answered immediately. "Miss you! Miss your company! Not a bit of it. As a matter of fact I've had company every bit as good as yours over the past week, and a good deal more consistent than yours usually is." She again smiled and assured me she was only kidding but added, "I've had Minnie coming over every morning to keep me company till late afternoon."

"You mean Tomini," I corrected her. "You mean old Trokka's woman, don't you?"

"Yes, that's right. Come on in and speak to her."

She led the way to the back veranda where I found Tomini, dressed in one of Mum's blue gingham dresses, busily stitching a rip in one of my shirts at the veranda table. "'Lo, Jimmy!" she greeted me, a big grin on her gentle old face.

"'Lo, Tomini. You work longa Missus now, eh?" I asked her.

"No more work, Jimmy," she answered with a laugh. "All the time do little fella bit work; all the time Missus give plenty tucker, all the time we eat, all the time talk. Me like this fella job longa Missus all the time."

"Oh, that's enough, Minnie!" Mum cut in to stem Tomini from handing out more praise. Then she sat down in the chair opposite her, and I went to my room.

When I was alone, I took from inside my shirt my headband gift from the Burunji tribe and hung it in my wardrobe. I then sat on the edge of my bed to ponder over my mother's state of health. Perhaps it would be more correct to say I sat there *worrying myself sick* over the shock I had received on seeing how, in the space of one week, her bodily health had changed so seriously I could no longer believe she would eventually recover from the sickness that was slowly consuming her. Despite her obvious attempts on my arrival home to convince me that all was well with her, I could not stay my conscience about the lies I had told over that cursed stick now waiting in the custody of old Bennatuk . . . waiting

. . . for God knows what . . . if that elusive man hiding up in the ranges ignored the summons of *his* god to give himself up for the tribal sentence of death to be carried out . . . what then?

I just had to do something. But I had to wait until the lengthening shadows of late afternoon sent Tomini back to the camp carrying a goodwill parcel of cake and lollies to share with her people. Only then was I able to speak to Mum in the kitchen, first with an offer to let me take over the meal she was trying so hard to prepare, in between bouts of weariness that kept making her sit down to rest. Being Mum, of course, she kept on declining my repeated offers of help with that same smile and, "Oh no, Jimmy—you have a right to expect at least one good meal prepared by me to celebrate your return home."

In the end she gave in and let me help her to her room to lie down while I took over the kitchen. Even so, the meal was a failure because she could only manage a cup of tea and I could only eat a mouthful or two.

And so I went to keep her company in her room. After I had given her a dose of the mixture she had in a bottle on the bedside table, she seemed to recover enough to sit up with a pillow I placed behind her at the bedhead. That done, I sat on the bed's edge and asked, "Mum, were you really happy all the time I was away?"

"Well, since you ask," she replied thoughtfully, "I was, at times, just a little apprehensive about what might happen to you, especially on the night when . . . Now let me see, what night was it . . ." She paused to recall the time and then said, "Ah, yes, it was on the fifth night after you left in the *Curlew* that it happened . . ." Again she tried to recollect the events of that night.

"What happened, Mum?" I interrupted her in my impatient wondering to find out—what?

"Now let me see, it was after nine o'clock and I was in bed with the lamp out," she went on. "Suddenly I got a queer . . . well, it was really a weird feeling that came over me when I heard, away over in the ranges, the howling of dingoes; it was like something echoing and re-echoing out of a nightmare, except that I was wide awake. I've never experienced anything like it in all my life, and I wouldn't want to have it happen ever again. It was dreadful, Jimmy."

"Then what happened, Mum?" I asked because I suddenly remembered what night it was she was talking about—the night that Kammaluk called out "Yarragul! . . . Yarragul! . . . Yarragul!" and the dingoes in the rain forest along the ranges had mournfully howled in reply.

She shrugged and said, "Nothing. After a while the weird feeling left me and I sensed, don't ask how, that you as well as Tajalli and Tajurra were safe and sound, so I went off to sleep." Her weariness returned, so I re-arranged her pillow and made her comfortable. I put my arms around her. "Goodnight, Mum," I whispered.

"Goodnight, son."

I blew out her lamp and went over to my room to try to sleep.

But sleep was out of the question in my emotional state of acute apprehension over what I had brought about by my inability to keep my nose out of things that did not really concern me. Even worse, to my worried mind, was what I had done to my mother by my lying and my conceit in believing that I could evade the consequences of my stupidity.

How easy it is to forget that in life, in all its facets of responsibilities and rewards, there are also many other things not explicable, as yet, to our human logic and reason. So many things are hidden from us that defy calm reasoning or logical explanation. One of them is the strange power possessed by the once wild tribes and even the present-day remnants of Australia's first people, the Aborigines, to will the destiny, through tribal justice, of any adult member of their tribe—or any other adult belonging to another tribe totemically related to them through the kinship of inter-tribal unions of their fully initiated men and women. Such inter-tribal unions of men and women also bestows upon them the full responsibility for everything they say or do that may affect the safety and welfare of their people. Banishment from these tribes can be one form of tribal justice for their breaking of tribal law. Being "sung" to death can be the supreme penalty that the elders decide a tribal offender must face in the expiation of his responsibility for a serious crime.

It was the enactment of this punishment I was to witness, and which I've often wished I had not; but emotion is causing me to leap ahead in the telling of my story.

After lunch on the second day following my arrival home from Burunji territory, Tajurra and I took the rations over to the camp and piled them in the camp's centre for distribution when the tribespeople returned later that afternoon. We, Tajurra and I, knew that down under the pandanus palms, Tajalli and the elders were in conclave; but neither of us had any desire to go down there because of that ominous bone, which we knew would be hanging there over the proceedings. Perhaps our imaginations were made more acute by the weird atmosphere that haunted the deserted mia-mias throughout the camp. Perhaps. But there was no denying the unusual behaviour of old Nellie harnessed to the dray. She was snorting and tossing her head while pawing with her front hooves at the ground in such a manner as to make it all I could do to hold her by the bridle until Tajurra got up on the dray and took the reins; even then I just managed to jump clear as she ploughed ahead dragging the dray with the brake on!

I leapt on to the dray beside Tajurra, holding on like grim

death to the reins. Nellie could not be restrained until we got clear of the camp; even then she was very agitated and wild-eyed with fear of—God knows what. It was a relief to get back to the home paddock and let her go.

After we had put the harness away we sat on the edge of the shed work-table talking and looking out of the wide open window that gives a panoramic view of the area along the creek bank from the bend of the creek away up in the direction of Cannon Ball Rock.

I said to Tajurra, "What for that pirralulla mia-mia still there?" and pointed over at the creek bend where it stood.

He shrugged and without any urging from me answered, "Me tell you before—Burunji man come there by and by."

"He stop, live longa that mia-mia?" I asked innocently. I did not then appreciate the significance of the elders deliberately leaving it there as an inducement for someone to enter it.

"No more stop, live there, Jimmy," he answered. "Maybe 'im stop longa mia-mia one night; longa another daytime 'im see something longa ground, longa that mia-mia, get 'im big fright; 'im run back longa bush where 'im live longa nobody all the time."

"What 'im do then?" I asked.

I got a non-committal shrug for an answer, so I said, "You got big fella worry now, Tajurra, eh? What for?"

"No more like talk longa that man any more, Jimmy. By and by 'im come soon, stop longa that mia-mia." As he spoke, he kept glancing out of the window to look along the creek bank and back at me in an obviously scared manner.

"Tajurra," I insisted. "What that man see by and by longa ground longa that mia-mia?"

Poor Tajurra! He had little option but to satisfy my wondering about the fate of this strange Aboriginal who, I had gathered, had lived for many years alone, an outcast

154

wandering the ranges. However, I had no need to guess at his identity because Tajurra blurted it out. "That man Yarragul, Jimmy! Suppose 'im go longa that mia-mia, sleep longa there, by and by longa morning 'im see track belonga Kadiatcha shoe all about mia-mia; then 'im close up finish. By and by 'im die longa hills."

To persist in questioning Tajurra was something, at least, I had the sense not to continue. He was about to say something, but he looked out of the open window and paused when his eyes had turned to focus away up along the creek bank . . . Then he whispered, "Look, Jimmy!" He stepped to the open window with me alongside him and we gazed up among the trees along the track that follows the creek bank . . . Again he whispered, "See 'im, Jimmy? Look! Look! 'Im stand longa tree."

But I could not see anything, so I said, "Wait! Me back soon." I raced over the rise to the house and came back with my father's high-powered binoculars. "Where 'im now?" I asked.

"Sit down now, longa tree."

I focused the glasses to my eyes and slowly scanned the distant track until at last I got the man in view, about half a mile along the track, sitting at the foot of a big forest mahogany tree. The bluish sheen around him, caused by the lens not being powerful enough at that distance to etch him in sharp detail, made me lower the glasses and wait.

Tajurra obviously wanted to get away from the shed because he backed away from the window to the open door. Then he said, "Jimmy, suppose 'im tell you what you do, suppose you look longa piccaninny daylight longa that mia-mia longa morning, you do it, eh, please?"

"Do what?" I asked.

"Put 'im thing Bennatuk make for you longa head."

"What for?"

"Suppose you look, see what Oona old men do, no more get debbil-debbil come longa you, suppose you wear 'im that thing, Jimmy."

I said, "All right, Tajurra, suppose me wear 'im thing longa head longa piccaninny daylight, longa morning, me be all right, eh?"

He nodded, but in an unsure way, and said, "More better you no more let old men see you look longa them longa morning, Jimmy. More better you no more look any time."

Then he left me to my own devices because he well knew that he had done his best to warn me not to interfere in something that he himself had no desire at all to be involved in . . .

I stood at that window for a good two hours more before the man, as I saw him through the glasses, rose and came walking closer and closer along the track through the trees until he reached the bend of the creek bank and paused there on the track a short distance from the pirralulla mia-mia. Then he turned full face in my direction to look warily about him. In that instant he came into full view in the glasses. He was a tall, heavily built grey-bearded giant of a man, without the usual headband of an adult Aboriginal, and . . . unarmed—not even a nulla-nulla in his hand. And there, in full view, I saw the cicatriced Z marks on his upper arms and chest—Yarragul, the murderer of Turrapini, had answered the call to be present at the penultimate chapter of his wanderings that would bring him to the end of his life.

Then I watched him turn and walk slowly across to the mia-mia . . . There he paused to look at the skeleton head of the baby dolphin, which was still there atop the stick driven into the ground by old Trokka to support it. Suddenly Yarragul knelt down and touched that emblem of his god. As he did so I saw his lips moving in what was in all probability a form of prayer. This, of course, was unbearable to me. Then he crept into the mia-mia out of sight . . . An overwhelming feeling of sadness seized me.

Holding back my tears, I left the shed, leaving the binoculars on the table, and went home. I had to see to my mother.

"To lie awake in the dead hours of the night; To play host to ghost thoughts: Unseen things—just beyond the light . . ." Those lines of the poem I knew so well were indeed totally apt in describing that night when I lay tossing and turning, unable to sleep. Like an Aboriginal with his night fire to ward off debbil-debbils, I, too, had to keep my room lamp burning low to help me ward off an indescribable urge to brood on spectres from the past. The gravestones of my grandparents, Ebenezer and Agnes Brent, standing under the coolibah trees just over the rise from the house, kept looming up in my thoughts. They, surely, must have had on their conscience the crime of needlessly killing the Oona leader and his woman, back in 1895, and must have carried to their graves the responsibility for what had since happened to the Oona people.

Then my thoughts would swing to that other grim tragedy ruthlessly inflicted on the Burunji people by those white men twenty-five or so years before.

Throughout that night, every hour, every half hour, my grandfather's clock in the front room broke the silence with its whirring followed by the soft boom of its chiming gong.

The harder I tried to sleep the more insistent became my emotional state of acute awareness that I was being drawn irresistibly by a powerful force to remain awake . . . Then the clock began to whir its warning of the coming counting of the hour . . . I listened to the gong . . . one . . . two . . . three . . . four . . . five—five o'clock! I could stand it no longer. I got up, put on my slippers and blue dressing-gown. Then I took out from my wardrobe the Burunji headband, put it on and blew out the lamp.

In the darkness, to avoid waking my mother by walking through the house, I climbed out of my window, tiptoed across the veranda and swung over the railings to be met by our dog Trudy, who had been transferred with her long exercise rope to my side of the house. The dog just nuzzled against me but made no sound as I gave her a pat and went on up over the rise and down the other side, heading for the saddle-shed, under the compulsive urging of that mysterious force that was drawing me on in spite of myself. I believe now that had I wanted to retreat back to the house, I would have been totally incapable of doing so.

In the pre-dawn darkness I reached the shed and went in. Oddly enough, I had absolutely no feeling of curiosity as to why I should be there—just that peculiar sensation of being acutely aware that I *must* do what that strange force was prompting me to do . . .

I sat on the edge of the table facing the open window to wait . . . How long I sat there I don't know; but across the darkness I could see the glowing embers of a fire in front of the pirralulla mia-mia . . .

Time passed to the point of a sudden emergence of the false dawn which usually precedes the "piccaninny daylight" of the true dawn . . . Soon the brief light retreated back to darkness for what seemed a long time to me . . . Then a soft grey suffusion in the eastern sky moved slowly, almost imperceptibly, into the chill pre-dawn greyness of another day . . .

I picked up the glasses and trained them on the mia-mia . . . just in time to see a figure emerge through the trees from the rear of the camp. It was Tajalli, in lap-lap, headband, and his body painted in the same white designs used by the Burunjis. In his right hand he carried his turtle emblem shield and in his left hand was a green she-oak branch tufted and tied in the fashion of a birch broom.

He paused at the edge of the cleared space facing the mia-mia. I had the glasses trained on him and, even in the dim grey light, I saw him lay the shield front down on the ground and the she-oak broom beside it. Next, he took from the Oonas' sacred bag he had tied to the back of the shield, the things I had once seen him use in the exorcising of debbil-debbils from the Oonas' sacred Bora Ring—they were Kadiatcha shoes—feathered, round-bottomed shoes, fashioned from bloodwood gum and eagle feathers.

He slipped his feet into the shoes, picked up his shield in his left hand and the broom in the other. In a peculiar rolling gait he moved, crouched forward, shield and broom in his hands, the dozen or so paces that took him to within about three feet of the rounded side of the mia-mia. There he turned to face the creek bank and began, in that semi-crouched stance, to step out each pace in that same peculiar rolling gait caused by the rounded bottoms of the feathered shoes.

He made the round of the mia-mia to come back to his starting point; there he turned to face the side of the mia-mia and he began to step backwards. At each backward step, he bent forward with the broom and brushed the ground to remove his tracks. Then at the edge of the trees, he stopped, took off the Kadiatcha shoes, put them back in the bag and ran, shield and broom clutched in his hands, to a group of dark figures just coming into view through the glasses.

In my absorption in watching Tajalli, I had at first failed to notice the six-man group, Trokka in the lead, who were swarming up from down on my right, from the vicinity of the camp. They also wore lap-laps and headbands, and their bodies were painted like Tajalli's.

They assembled directly in line with me and the distant

mia-mia. In the slowly increasing grey dawnlight, I saw Tajalli put down his broom and the shield, to take from his bag another item that I had good reason to dread from my own experience of it—the long human-hair cord with that dreadful thigh bone of a native tiger cat rolled up inside it.

Moving the six elders away from the shield and broom, Tajalli formed them into a single line about a yard apart, facing the mia-mia. Then he unrolled the cord into loops in his hand and placed the bone on the ground directly in front of Trokka, whose lips were moving in some incantation as he slowly bent and picked it up as Tajalli stepped to his right side. The moment he did that, the six men behind crouched down in a queer bent-kneed stance, each man lifting his right foot to allow Tajalli to draw the cord under it as he passed from one man to the next until he reached the last man in the line. Then he himself took his position with the cord between his legs and drew it up over his back and right shoulder to grasp the end in his right hand.

In the cold grey dawnlight the effect of Tajalli's turning his back to me was that temporarily he merged into the greyness when he turned to face the line of crouching men and his white frontal body markings were no longer visible to make him stand out in stark skeletal clarity.

Keeping him in the focus of the glasses I saw him crouch in that queer bent-kneed stance like the six men in front of him ... Then I heard a low but piercing sound on the chill dawn air; it was an almost indescribable sound; it affected me as though I were sitting in a darkened cathedral and was suddenly struck by a swift staccato organ note of brief but painful intensity. Then I saw the line of men begin a peculiar bent-kneed "dance", moving sideways from one foot to the other in a rhythmic swaying, and, in that chill dawnlight, I heard the low weird hissing "song" that was being chanted softly but insistently as the "dance" proceeded.

Training the glasses up front I got Trokka in sharp focus—his left hand was held high as he chanted and he kept moving it backwards and forwards in a slow throwing action towards the pirralulla mia-mia. In his outstretched right hand he held that bone taut on its cord and pointed directly at the mia-mia.

In the few minutes that it took to complete the death sentence on the man in that mia-mia, I was totally unconscious of anything but a dreadful compulsion to see the thing out to its end. It came swiftly. Suddenly the chanting stopped. The elders literally took to their heels and ran for the camp as though the devil himself were after them.

Tajalli stood there all alone. Then I watched him wind the cord back around the bone and replace it in its bag on the shield. Then he picked up the shield and the broom and taking one last look around him he began to walk away slowly,

head bowed, and I knew he was crying. He continued down and disappeared into the outskirts of trees at the rear of the camp.

Suddenly all the agony of that sleepless night culminating in my compulsion to be present to witness a man being "sung" to death broke over me and I lost control . . . I, too, broke down and cried as I had never cried before and I hope to God I never shall again.

I could no longer bring myself ever to look again at that silent mia-mia standing on the bend of the creek bank, mute witness to a tragedy brought upon the Aborigines by white men who had achieved nothing by their greed but the destruction of human life.

I took off my headband and slipped it into the pocket of my dressing-gown. That done, I managed to regain control of myself and dry my tears.

With the glasses in my hand I walked from the shed into the oncoming sunrise, and made my way back to the house.

To avoid disturbing my mother when I reached the house, I tiptoed around the side-veranda, climbed into my room through the open window and put the binoculars on my table. Then a faint "Jimmy!" sent me running over to the open doorway of Mum's bedroom. She was lying there in bed, staring at me as though she was emerging from the grip of a nightmare. She tried to sit up and I reached her before she could collapse back on the pillow. She gasped, "Jimmy, the medicine!"

Frantic with fear, I managed to get her into a sitting position with the pillow supporting her before I turned my attention to the bottle and measuring glass on the table . . . I poured the dose into the glass . . . it barely reached the amount specified on the bottle's label—the last dose!

Holding her with my arm around her shoulders, I managed to get her to take the dose. Then she lay back with her eyes closed; she sighed an ineffably weary sigh and remained still for upwards of five minutes before the mixture took effect. She opened her eyes and said, "Oh, Jimmy, what have I ever done to deserve this terrible sickness that won't leave me no matter what I do to try to get over it? Surely God can't want me to suffer like this for nothing. There must be some reason for it."

"I don't know, Mum!" I tried comforting her. "Maybe the reason for it all lies in something beyond our understanding. Maybe we should get you to Cairns to see a doctor; the medicine is all done, so we'll just have to get you to a doctor."

She nodded and said, "All right, son, if I don't feel any

better by ten o'clock we'll go to Cairns, so you had better get the boat ready in case. But I wouldn't mind a cup of tea if you'd get me one, and find yourself something to eat too."

"OK, Mum, will do."

In the kaleidoscope of our daily lives how often does a miracle occur that we are never aware of? Even if we were aware of it, would we ever be able to reason its hidden purpose in the controlling of our destinies?

On that memorable morning I watched, waited and saw a miracle occur before my very eyes.

I had lit the stove and got the fire going to boil the kettle. Then I made the tea and took a cup into Mum but she didn't drink it because she was sound asleep. L just tiptoed back to the kitchen with it and no sooner had I put it on the kitchen table than Tajurra appeared in the doorway. "'Lo, Jimmy," he whispered. "All right me come in?"

I nodded. He came in and sat in his usual place alongside my chair at the end of the table.

"You want toast?" I asked. He did, so I made a thick four-slice batch on the toast-rack in the front of the stove's fire-box, and sat with him to eat it with marmalade and the tea.

Before he began to eat he said, "Tajalli tell me tell you mother belonga you no more get sick by and by, Jimmy."

"How Tajalli know mother belonga me get sick all the time, Tajurra?" I asked, because Tajalli had not been near the house since our return from Burunji territory.

"Dunno, Jimmy, 'im know all right; maybe 'im know when you tell 'im about mother belonga you see that bad fella talk stick. Tajalli talk longa Trokka, longa old men about it. Tajalli say tell you he make talk longa Burunji old men soon, tell 'im burn bad fella stick, stop mother belonga you get sick all the time."

And as a final encouragement to me, Tajurra said, "Mother belonga you no more die now, Jimmy. We eat this good fella tucker, go longa veranda, look longa Tajalli make smoke talk, eh?"

I eagerly agreed and we ate the toast, washed it all down with the tea and then made our way around to the side veranda to watch. Standing outside the open gunroom window I could also see across to Mum's open door to keep an eye on her too.

Across at the camp the whole tribe were missing. We could see them streaming north along the beach until they disappeared from view around Rocky Point.

Only old Trokka, a burning firestick in his hand, and Tajalli beside him were left on the beach by the pandanus palms fronting the camp. A piled, unlit fire was ready at their feet. In Tajalli's hands was the square of bark used for sending the alternating puffs and spirals from the smoking fire that Trokka now lit by thrusting his firestick into the base of the piled wood.

For several minutes the two men just stood there . . . then suddenly Trokka touched Tajalli on the shoulder to begin the message. In the dead still morning air Tajurra and I watched the sending of the first message to the Burunjis . . . then there was a pause while Tajalli waited for the answer.

As Tajurra and I waited on the veranda I looked around, through the open gunroom window, across to my mother's bedroom. . . . To my amazement she was getting up. My first impulse was to race around to help her but something stopped me.

While Tajurra kept his gaze fixed on the two men at the fire, I watched my mother kneel down, her hands clasped before her in prayer . . . and the miracle of that morning began to unfold.

Tajurra whispered, "Look, Jimmy," and pointed in the direction of the two men. While my mother went on praying to *her* god, Trokka and Tajalli began to set in motion the message on the smoke talk to let the Burunjis know that Yarragul had obeyed the summons of *his*.

In a minute or so it was all over. We saw Tajalli send the final part of the message for the Burunjis to burn the evil talk stick to placate their god, the great dolphin in the sky, so that the last vestiges of its evil power could be lifted from the lives of the Brents as well as the Aborigines.

Tajalli dropped his bark square in the fire and turned with Trokka to look over at the house. Then they walked into the concealing shade of the pandanus palms.

"Jimmy!"

Tajurra and I swung around to see Mum standing at the gunroom doorway in her yellow dressing-gown.

She was smiling her familiar bright smile and before I could get over my shock at seeing her apparently well and happy again, she said, "Well, who's going to help me get a nice hot breakfast ready?" And she went on over to the kitchen. Tajurra and I joined her there with a babble of talk and excitement at her recovery. She soon put a stop to our excited chattering with a "Now then, I want some more wood for bread-baking later. So, while you two are getting it, I'll use what's here in the wood-box to get breakfast cooked."

"OK, Mum." "OK, Missus." Tajurra and I agreed and raced outside to get the wood she needed.

Some would decry the miracle that my friend Tajurra and I witnessed that morning, and probably I, too, might have done the same had it not been that my own mother, a devout Christian, had prayed for deliverance from the thing that was slowly destroying her while, at the very same time, the so-called heathen Aborigines were asking their god to save the "White Missus". That I do know for certain—Tajurra told me so, long after the whole unhappy business was over and done with.

*

166

It certainly was a real pleasure for Tajurra and me to sit down with Mum in the kitchen that morning to eat the breakfast she prepared. She herself ate heartily and clearly showed that she was on the way to recovering her former good health. And she had no trouble in getting us two boys to continue with the chopping and stacking of the firewood she needed for her bread-baking and more besides.

But it was round about ten that morning when Tajurra stopped his work at the woodheap to walk up to the top of the rise. He stopped there for a while looking over in the direction of the pirralulla mia-mia. Then suddenly he beckoned me to come up with a "Jimmy, hurry!"

Despite not wanting ever to look again at that silent memento of human folly, I did go up to satisfy my curiosity. Standing there with Tajurra I followed his hand pointing at the track heading out along the creek bank in the direction of Cannon Ball Rock . . . There, head down and travelling in a peculiar short-stepping, jumping gait was Yarragul. In silence we watched him heading out for the distant ranges and the place he would select to lay himself down to will himself to die. Suddenly he disappeared among the trees in the distance . . . Yarragul's life was over . . . Somewhere out there in those ranges his skeleton lies hidden to this day.

Both Tajurra and I were too emotionally upset to say anything. We went back to our wood chopping: two boys travelling fast on the road to becoming grown up by learning from the bitterness of the past what we hoped we would never again have to endure because of our folly.

The rest of the day ended quietly. In the living-room that night I sat with Mum on the settee, neither of us aware that with us in the room lay the clue to a partial unravelling of a secret that will never have a full explanation. The very means by which we were drawn to find that partial unravelling has no logical explanation either.

But there were other events that had to be finalised first.

Late in the afternoon of the third day after the Pointing of the Bone had been carried out, there arrived on Oonaderra the same three-man, one-woman party led by the Burunji leader Kammaluk. Their main purpose now was to exhume the bones of Turrapini from the big stringybark at Cannon Ball Rock for proper and final tree-burial on Burunji territory. There was another reason for their visit but I had to wait to find out from Tajalli what it was.

Prior to the Burunji arrival I had watched Tajalli and old Trokka building a pile of wood for a corroboree fire to be held that night within the circle of coral lumps that enclose the Oonas' sacred Bora Ring almost directly opposite the house over at the top of the slope leading down to the beach. The purpose of the corroboree was to be the lifting of the taboo curse on Cannon Ball Rock and the giant stringybark tree holding the bones of Turrapini.

About an hour before sundown I was in the gunroom with the binoculars trained through the open north window. Coming from the camp, in single file, were six of the Oona elders with Tajalli in the lead and old Trokka directly behind him. All were in lap-laps and headbands but Tajalli was also carrying his sacred shield in his right hand and his human-hair bag of sacred objects was hanging by its loop from his neck.

As they passed from view from the north window I stepped over to the east window and picked them up again in the glasses as they approached the Bora Ring. There they paused outside the circle of coral lumps. Then Tajalli, followed by Trokka, stepped inside the Bora Ring itself. Tajalli laid his shield and bag on the ground some six feet away from the covering of pandanus leaves in the centre of the inner circle with the six red, dome-shaped brain corals holding down the

168

palm fronds' cover.

They removed the brain corals, then the concealing palm fronds and . . . clearly through the binoculars I saw the sacred stone of the Oonas—an ebony black meteorite—come into sharp focus. The sacred Oona god, the great turtle, was on it—etched into its oval-shaped, six-foot-long surface in fragmented pearl shell, while all around the turtle were whorls and geometric patterns all etched into the stone in the same scintillating fragmented pearl shell.

The moment I had the Bora Stone in focus I lost it, while the elders, at the moment of its uncovering, swarmed into the inner circle to surround the ancient relic of their god and to shut it away from the scrutiny of everyone but themselves. As a further precaution, the piled heap of wood prepared by Tajalli and Trokka that day was, I think, intentionally built as a screen between the stone and the eyes of the white people in the house of the Brents.

I saw Trokka bend down at the other side of the stacked wood and . . . in an instant the pile leapt into a roaring wall of flames completely shutting out everything from my prying eyes. So there I had to abandon all further attempts at trying to find out what went on until the small hours of the next morning.

When I woke the next day it was already sun-up. I dressed and went into the gunroom and picked up the binoculars and focused through the east window over the Bora Ring. But the Oonas were just leaving. Their corroboree fire had been put out and the pandanus palm fronds were back in place over the sacred Bora Stone with the red dome-shaped brain corals holding them in place.

I watched Tajalli with his bag and shield lead the old men back towards the camp. So I went and lit the stove in readiness for Mum to cook breakfast.

169

No sooner had I lit the stove when Tajurra arrived on the back veranda to call softly, "Jimmy."

I went out to find him all excited and telling me to "Bring 'im glasses, Jimmy, quick; Burunji people go soon get bones longa that tree longa Cannon Ball Rock."

I went and got the binoculars and followed him up to the top of the rise. Tajurra didn't need the binoculars, but I used them to look across to the pirralulla mia-mia where I saw the Burunjis, carrying spears and wearing lap-laps and headbands, standing with Trokka who was holding a lighted firestick alongside Tajalli. All were watching the woman who had travelled with the Burunjis making her way up along the track. Through the glasses I could clearly see the blanket bundle she was carrying over her left shoulder and, most significant of all, in her right hand she was carrying a woven string dilly-bag to carry the bones of Turrapini. It is always an Aboriginal woman who traditionally carries the last remains of any member of her tribe to their final resting place. One of the men of the Burunji party would scale the stringybark to collect those bones for her.

When the woman was out of earshot of the pirralulla mia-mia she stopped and stood facing away from the men watching her.

That was the signal for Kammaluk to bend down and pick up the skull of the baby dolphin which he wrapped in a piece of bark. He stepped back with his two Burunji men out of the way of Tajalli who pulled out the stick that had supported the skull and threw it into the low opening of the mia-mia. Trokka then stepped forward and thrust the firestick into the thatch of the mia-mia. Almost instantly the entire thing exploded into flames and collapsed in a shower of sparks and flames.

Without further ado, Kammaluk turned, said something to the others and they set off up along the track to carry out their last act of retrieving Turrapini's remains before travelling on to their own tribal territory.

I nudged Tajurra and said, "You want eat tucker longa house?"

"Too right," he answered. And down we went to find Mum already in the kitchen preparing the breakfast.

"All right if Tajurra stays for breakfast, Mum?" I asked her.

She smiled and said to us, "As long as he doesn't mind hashmagandi he's welcome to sit and bog in with us."

Tajurra didn't mind at all having cold stew from the day before, re-cooked into a hot (hashmagandi) curry. His "Gee, Missus, you all the same longa me like 'im Noola." (He used the tribal name of Noola to describe his own mother.)

Mum just laughed and said, "More better you say nice thing longa Noola, too, eh?"

He nodded shyly and we all sat down at Mum's bidding of "All right, the pair of you, just sit yourselves down and let the food stop your blarney while I make the tea."

It was so good to be, as I imagined we were, free at last from all the consequences that had followed my finding of that evil thing that had lain so long in my grandfather's old tin trunk. But the ending of the story had not been reached for us Brents, for there was more.

Round about four that afternoon my mother, completely recovered, was doing some housework in the living-room while Tajurra and I were having a rest from the wood-chopping. We sat at the back veranda table eating the smoke-o of brownie slices and drinking the orange cordial Mum had served us. Suddenly Tajalli appeared at the back steps in his khaki rig-out. There was a tell-tale bulge of something inside his shirt. We exchanged his greeting of "'Lo, Jimmy, 'lo, Tajurra," and he came up and stood at the veranda entrance.

"You want see 'im Missus, Tajalli?" I asked.

171

"By and by," he answered. Then he took from his shirt a message stick! Both Tajurra and I gasped at the sight of it dangling from its cord as he held it up for us to see the carvings all over it with the Burunji tribal Z dominating the carved message which was otherwise totally unintelligible to my eyes.

I found my voice and whispered, "No, Tajalli! Me no more want that bad fella talk stick longa this house; you tell me Burunji man by and by burn that bad fella thing."

He smiled and for the first time in his life he came and sat with us and placed the object on the table. Tajurra and I stared at it . . . then I looked at it more closely . . . it was not the stick I had found in my grandfather's old tin trunk. For one thing it did not have a human-hair carrying cord—this one was woven from palm fibre and closely resembled human hair . . . And another thing—the more I looked at it the more I felt a sense of peace steal over me. Tajurra became seized by the same feeling because he looked at Tajalli and said, "This fella stick all the same good fella stick, eh?"

Tajalli grinned, helped himself to a slice of the brownie and then told us that the stick was indeed a "good fella stick". It had been brought to Oonaderra by Kammaluk specially for "white fella Missus and white fella Jimmy" to thank us for our help in lending our boat for the visit to the Burunji tribe.

In brief, Tajalli explained to us that the other stick had been destroyed. This new stick was intended to be a memento of the visit, and all the goodwill of Kammaluk's people was embodied in its carved message of hope and good wishes for the future of the "white fella Missus and white fella Jimmy".

Tajalli finished eating his slice of brownie and said to me, "Me go now, Tajurra go now, back longa camp, Jimmy. Suppose you give mother belonga you this fella talk stick, eh? You no more tell 'im about Burunji men burn other one, eh?"

"OK," I answered as he and Tajurra stood up and walked

to the steps; there they paused briefly to bid me "So long, Jimmy". I said, "See you by and by." And they left in the lengthening shadows cast by the trees in the westering sun.

I picked up the talk stick and went to tell Mum that Tajalli had brought it back for her. But she was busy in her room and she said, "Later, Jimmy. I'm trying to get my work finished before dinner. Get me some wood in, please, and get the stove going."

"OK, Mum." I dropped the stick on the living-room table on my way out to the woodheap and there it lay until after dinner when we went into the living-room. I lit the hanging lamp above the living-room table, then I picked up the stick and went and sat with her on the settee. She took the stick to examine its intricate carvings and for a while we just sat there discussing it . . . Suddenly everything became still and silent. For a moment or two we just sat there wondering at the unusual quietness . . . then she said, "Jimmy, the clock's stopped. But that's funny—I only wound it up this morning. I probably didn't wind it enough. You go and wind it up properly."

"OK, Mum."

I went to my grandfather's clock standing in the corner of the room, opened its glass-faced door and bent to pull the knob on the little drawer at the base of the clock to open it and get the clock's winding-key out. The drawer stuck at my first pull so I gave it a sharper pull and it came out, spilling its contents of odds and ends on the floor. I salvaged the winding-key from among them and knelt down to return the things to the drawer and to replace it . . . I was about to do so when my fingers felt something on the back of the drawer. I turned it round and . . . there held to the back of the drawer by a screw through its open end was a small brass key. "Hey, Mum! Look what's here."

She came over and looked at the key held by the screw.

"Well, what on earth would that be doing there?" she asked.

"I think I can guess, Mum," I answered.

"What?"

"I bet it belongs to that log-book in Grand-dad's old trunk."

"All right then," she answered. "You wind the clock while I get a screw-driver and get that key off."

I tried to wind the clock but it was almost fully wound. So I took the screw-driver Mum brought from the kitchen and got the screw out and gave Mum the little brass key. Then I put everything back into the drawer and replaced it without further trouble. The moment the drawer slid back into its place the clock resumed its steady rhythmic "tick-tocking" again.

I, of course, was all eagerness to get the log-book to prove I had guessed right. But Mum made me sit with her while she thought the matter over. Eventually she said she was not at all sure we were doing the right thing by opening the log-book because, as she put it, "It may be better to let sleeping dogs lie, Jimmy."

"Oh, Mum!" I argued. "That's silly! Why can't we just have one look inside that log-book and then I can put it back in that secret bottom of Grand-dad's trunk with the stick and then we can forget all about the whole thing. Come on, Mum, please!"

She finally relented and followed me into the gunroom where she put the key on the desk and lit the kerosene desk lamp. While I excitedly began to pile the trunk's contents on the floor she sat in Grand-dad's oaken swivel chair, silently watching me getting to the trunk's false bottom and there inserting my finger nail to lift it clear to reveal the brass-bound log-book. I handed it to her and came and stood at her side to watch her insert the key into the padlock. It unlocked easily. She withdrew the lock from the book's brass-clasps and put it on the desk. Her seemingly slow, deliberate movements stung me to say, "Oh, come on, Mum! Hurry up!"

She ignored my impatient eagerness and opened the book's cover to reveal a folded document between the cover and the book's first page. All impatience I watched as she opened the official legal document. In silence we read what it said:

"In accordance with Marine Regulation Codes and pursuant to Article E4, Clause 5 of Marine Insurance Requirements, We the undersigned, have registered and insured, for the sum of £12,000, the pearling lugger *Pandora* in the name of its Owner/Master *Jonathon Fordyce*, resident in Broome, Western Australia, at the date of the signing of this Document . . ."

The rest of the document set out the usual legal whys and wherefores that such papers always set out to protect whatever it is that wants protecting.

Mum put the paper to one side and in the quiet of that lamplit room we went through the daily entries that Jonathon Fordyce had recorded in his travels and journeys with the three men he had employed as crew who alternately did the air pumping and the deep sea diving in diving suits and helmets in their search of the sea bed for trochus shell and pearls.

It was not until we reached one entry that the identity of J.F. became apparent. It was dated: "October 4, 1919; Broome. Today we leave for Torres Strait to try our luck there in getting what we can in shell and—maybe—pearls. I've written to Ebenezer, my step-brother on Oonaderra cattle station to let him know I'll be sailing from Thursday Island before the Wet Season sets in and for him to expect me round about Christmas time with a supply of grog I'll be bringing to tide us over the festive season."

So the mysterious J.F. was none other than my step-great-uncle whom I had never even heard of as a relative. And the fact that my grandfather, Ebenezer Brent, had all along been expecting the arrival of his step-brother explained, to some degree, what must have gone on after Grand-dad found him wandering sick and almost blind that day out at Cannon Ball Rock. And the hiding of the message stick along with the log-book in the tin trunk was, obviously, to keep the secret from ever leaking out that Jonathon Fordyce was a multiple murderer, hence the fact that no one, except Mum and I, ever found out the white man's name or anything else about him.

The last entry in the log-book was dated "December 23, 1919. Thursday Island. We have not had a very successful run in Torres Strait; got little worthwhile shell and only a few seed pearls to show for all the work that was done. Leaving now, 7.30 a.m., for Oonaderra but we might try a bit of diving from one of the islands off the Great Barrier Reef on the way down to Oonaderra."

They did reach an island on the Great Barrier Reef—the one facing the Burunjis' camp on the mainland, and there began the indiscriminate massacre of blacks and whites that was the beginning of this sad story.

Mum made no comment on what we had read. She just folded the document, replaced it inside the log-book's cover and locked the padlock back in its clasps. Turning to me she said, "Jimmy, get that stick in the living-room and bring it here. We'll put it and the book back where we found it and then put the whole business out of our minds."

"Righto, Mum," I said and went and brought the message stick. I placed the two things and the key in the secret compartment and was on the point of piling Grand-dad's old diaries and things on top of the false bottom when Mum said, "Wait a moment, Jimmy. See if you can locate your grandfather's Nineteen-Twenty diary. I'd like to see what he had to say about that step-brother of his."

"OK," I answered and went through the old exercise

books that my grandfather had used to record the happenings on Oonaderra. It wasn't hard to find the one she wanted because there were exactly twenty-six of them—one for each year he had spent on Oonaderra between 1895 and 1920.

I got her the one she wanted and stood by her while she flicked open the cover to the first, and the one and only, page my Grand-dad had written on before his death:

"January 9, 1920. Found a white man some five days ago wandering on my property. He was almost blind and suffering from scrub fever. Nursed him over the fever but he has lost his memory and doesn't know how he got to be here. I'm sending him to Cooktown with old Charley (Tajalli) before the Wet Season sets in in earnest."

And that was probably one of the reasons why the white man had disappeared completely. My grandfather had not even admitted in his diary that he knew the man, and no one could have picked up tracks of any sort let alone tried to get into the backblocks of Cape York Peninsula during the incessant rain and floods of that year. Whatever tracks might have been left on that ground would have vanished for ever in this wilderness on the Cape once the Wet Season really set in.

Perhaps I should mention one other thing about my grandfather's Nineteen-Twenty diary—his last entry read: "January 27. Set a shotgun trap over under the big fig tree facing the Crossing on the creek bank opposite the Big Scrub. A huge boar has been crossing the creek there and killing calves on this side. I'm bound to get him sooner or later when he springs the trap and gets both barrels of my 12-gauge shotgun cartridges."

He never got that boar because the next morning he himself was trapped when he apparently crouched to get under the heavy undergrowth to check on the trap. He must have completely forgotten the cord stretched across the track and hitched taut to the triggers of both barrels of the shotgun.

The resulting blast of the gun brought Tajalli running from the camp to see what had happened. He found Grand-dad dead on the ground.

Mum said, "All right, Jimmy, put everything away. I'm going to make a cup of tea. And mind you, I don't want to hear any more about this awful business again. Do you understand?"

"Yes, Mum, I understand," I said and meant it.

A few days later Mort Chandler, the mailman, arrived with his loaded pack-horses carrying the mail. He didn't stay long. He just brought us our bundle of papers, magazines and letters, had a cup of tea and went on his way.

And it was Mum herself who broke her determination not to speak about the "awful business" of our reading the log-book and discovering its implications of our link with that business. She found in the copy of the *Cairns Post* Mort Chandler had brought along in the mail, a little item in the middle of that newspaper headlined, "Mystery man takes secret of his identity to his grave . . ."

It went on to say how a man, suffering from total amnesia, had never recovered his memory from whatever the ordeal was that he had suffered to find himself lost, sick and blind, in the vast wilderness of Cape York Peninsula. It also briefly mentioned the kind family who had befriended him and given him a home over the past twenty-six years... "R.I.P." And that was all.

Perhaps J.F. did pay for what he had done in his lifetime and perhaps he was glad to end his sufferings and be gone from it ... Perhaps.

As for me, well, the vista of the future seemed a whole lot better to go on living and working and hoping that we all, blacks and whites, could one day settle our differences and join hands in making a better world for us all.

GLOSSARY

Bail-up: Means, to most Australians, to be held up by either bushrangers (outlaws) or, more commonly, for any animal to be held at bay by hunting dogs.

Carapace: The shell of a turtle or a tortoise.

Cassowary: A large flightless bird somewhat resembling an ostrich; it inhabits the rain forest areas of Australia's east coast, now mainly from Cairns northwards along the coastline and as far inland as the ranges on Cape York Peninsula.

Coo-ee: The Australian bush call used for ascertaining someone's whereabouts; the sound carries over an extremely long distance.

Damper: A dough made from self-raising flour into a round "loaf" which is cooked by burying it in the ashes of a fire; it can also be cooked in a portable (circular, lidded) cast-iron camp oven.

Demijohn: A stone, cork-stoppered jar once used extensively as a container for rum, whisky etc.

Dob in: Means, in Australian slang, to tell tales against others to cause them trouble.

Flying fox: The Australian nocturnal fruit-eating bat. Its head and face closely resemble those of a fox.

Gympie-Gympie: A stinging tree that grows in the Australian rain forests on the northern tropical east coast. It can grow to a height of about 9 feet, and is soft-stemmed with large, bright green, heart-shaped leaves which are covered in microscopic "needles" loaded with a vicious, irritant poison. Brushing against its leaves can cause an agonizing

181

irritation in the skin which can last for months afterwards whenever the affected part comes into contact with cold water. Its second vicious effect is to cause nose-bleeding. When the trees are being cut down the needles are scattered in the air and can be inhaled if the workers are not wearing masks.

Headband: Worn only by some male Aborigines to denote their status of authority by virtue of the manhood and honour they have earned and proven to the satisfaction of the tribal elders who decide when to award this coveted "badge".

Hessian: A coarse fabric used mainly for making sacks, bags, aprons.

Kadiatcha shoes: Certain tribes believed that a death was invariably due to the evil magical influences of some enemy. When the guilt was fixed upon a particular person, either a man called Kadiatcha was chosen to avenge the death, or an individual would go forth on his own initiative wearing the shoes, which were made from blood, feathers and human-hair string and rounded at each end so as to make it impossible to distinguish from which direction the footprints came. The man whose mia-mia was encircled by the prints of the Kadiatcha knew that the bone had been "pointed" at him and invariably willed himself to die.

Lolly: An Australian abbreviation of lollipop, meaning sweets or candy.

Mia-mia: A thatched, beehive-shaped dwelling made of blady grass and pandanus leaves which individual families of a tribe use when they stay in a camp for a long while.

Myall: A wild Australian Aboriginal.

Pannikin: An enamelled mug used as a cup.

Pidgin English: From China throughout the South Seas there are quite a few variations of Pidgin English, evolved as a result of the advent of white traders and adventurers in search of booty in whatever form they could get it, including human beings bought or captured by the "blackbirders" of the old sailing-ship days. It was essential for those traders to be able to communicate to get their business done quickly, so Pidgin English became a mongrel, few-word means of two-way communication between native peoples and their white exploiters. The Australian version of Pidgin was created mainly by the first white settlers when trying to enlist the Aborigines into their unpaid work force. They established a unique form of Pidgin that can be described as the simplest, most direct form of all the variants of this convenience language of quick communication. In this novel the Australian Pidgin has been simplified for the sake of young readers who may find it difficult and strange.

Pointing of the Bone: This was practised by many Aboriginal tribes. A man wishing to use a "pointing bone" would go into the bush, place the bone in the ground and repeat curses over it. During the night it would be pointed at the victim and magic chants sung over it. The victim would invariably sicken and die.

Scrub dingo: The same species as the Australian wild dog, except that this animal lives in the scrub (rain forest) and has evolved into a larger, reddish-haired animal of greater cunning and ferocity.

Skite: A boaster, a braggart, a show-off.

Walkabout: The Aborigines of Cape York Peninsula go Walkabout usually for the duration of the Wet. They leave their settled camp to go in search of different food to supplement their diet, for example, waterbirds' eggs and lily buds. The Walkabout is also a bartering trip between tribes, and a time when young initiated men and women of compatible tribes are exchanged.

The Wet and the Dry: The Wet usually, but not always, lasts from about the beginning of January to the middle of April; and the Dry usually extends from about April until the end of the year. Occasional rain falls in the Dry.

Yam stick: A pointed hardwood stick used by Aboriginal women for digging up yam tubers which are cooked and used as a vegetable to accompany meat or fish.

Yugari: A bivalve mollusc. It lives in a flattish, hinged, triangular-shaped white shell and grows to approximately the size of a mussel. Its main habitat is in the Great Barrier Reef waters.